CW00959286

ERRATA

(1) Figures 4.5, 4.6 and 4.7 (pages 80–85 inclusive). The labels on the 'St 1' and 'St 3' lines should be interchanged.

(2) Page 100. In the equation '$P_{stat}^{-0.1}$' should read '$P_{stat} - 0.1$'.

(3) Page 103. In Figure 5.6, the '200' on the V (m^3) horizontal axis should be one position earlier.

(4) Page 104. In Figure 5.7 the '20' on the V (m^3) horizontal axis should be one position earlier, and all the lines on the graph have been drawn too far along. The top five should end at 100 m^3, not at 200 m^3, and the lowest line should end at 10 m^3, not 20 m^3. (The same figure as drawn on page 108 is correct, except that the P_{red} values should be in the vertical order 0.4, 0.6, 0.8, 1, 1.2.)

(5) Figure 6.8 (page 123). On the horizontal axis, '15000' should read '1500'.

(6) Page 129, five lines down. ' ... an L/D ratio is equal to 16 and the actual distance in metres = 0.5 × 16 = 8.0 m' should read ' ... an L/D ratio is equal to 11 and the actual distance in metres = 0.5 × 11 = 5.5 m'.

(7) Pages 98–101. Figures 5.4 and 5.5. The order on the horizontal axes of the left hand parts of the nomographs should be (from right to left) 0.01, 0.1, 1, 10.

GUIDE TO DUST EXPLOSION PREVENTION AND PROTECTION

Part 1 — Venting

Second Edition

Geoff Lunn

Dusty errors

The second edition of the book *Dust explosion prevention and protection, part 1—venting* was published by the Institution in October 1992. It soon became clear that, in spite of careful proof-reading, there were several printing errors. An erratum slip was prepared and included in copies sold subsequently. Nevertheless, some copies have escaped uncorrected, and the Health & Safety Executive—in the form of technology and health science division director Adrian Ellis —has written expressing concern and pointing out one more error.

So, all past buyers of the book are being mailed a new erratum slip. If you have a copy of the book, please stick the slip into it and note particularly the small but crucial errors on pages 80, 82, 84, 103 and 104. If you have not received a slip by the end of November, please contact Jacqueline Cressey in Rugby. Thank you.

The Chemical Engineer, 25 November 1993

INSTITUTION OF CHEMICAL ENGINEERS

This Guide is published and recommended by the Institution of Chemical Engineers as a valuable contribution to safety. The information in the Guide is given in good faith and belief in its accuracy, but does not imply the acceptance of any legal liability or responsibility whatsoever, by the Institution, the author or by individual members of the Steering Committee for the consequences of its use or misuse in any particular circumstances.

Published by
Institution of Chemical Engineers
Davis Building
165–171 Railway Terrace
Rugby, Warwickshire CV21 3HQ, UK.

Copyright © 1992 Institution of Chemical Engineers

ISBN 0 85295 293 7

First Edition 1984
Second Edition 1992

Printed in England by Stephen Austin/Hertford

PREFACE

The first edition of this IChemE guide, *Dust explosion prevention and protection. Part I — Venting,* by Dr C. Schofield, was published in 1985. It formed the first authoritative and comprehensive guidance for venting published in the UK in a form that was accessible to engineers, scientists, safety specialists and managers.

Since 1985, however, much new information on the estimation of venting requirements has been published and it was felt that this new information required incorporation in a new edition of the guide. This second edition of the explosion venting guide aims to introduce the new knowledge in an easily comprehended form and with a full description of its relationship with methods familiar from the original document. These familiar methods are fully described in the new text, and this edition stands on its own as a complete document. The reader will need to make no reference to the original guide.

The recommendations presented in this guide will provide a basis for good practice in the protection, by venting, of plant and processes wherein dust explosions could occur. The guide aims to help those responsible for the design, supply and operation of plant to comply with the provisions of the Health and Safety at Work Act and the Factories Act.

This guide assumes on the part of the reader some basic knowledge of dust explosions and their potential. If you are unsure where to start, the Institution of Chemical Engineers is able to advise on consultancies and laboratories that can offer assistance.

It must be recognized that on occasions strict adherence to these recommendations would be inappropriate and further advice may have to be sought. In addition it would be expected that further research and other developments will lead to improved methods and it is not the intention that this guide should inhibit such developments.

The author wishes to thank all the members of the IChemE Steering Committee for their invaluable help and guidance, and Mrs Lynne Swindells of the typing office of the Explosion and Flame Laboratory, Buxton, for her hard work.

The assistance of the Health and Safety Executive in funding the writing of this guide is gratefully acknowledged.

MEMBERSHIP OF THE STEERING COMMITTEE

J.A. Barton (Chairman)	Health and Safety Executive
F. Cairns	Dust Control Equipment Limited
D. Crowhurst	Fire Research Station
N. Gibson	Burgoyne Consultants Limited
W. Hamm	Consultant
P.E. Moore	Kidde-Hartnell
R.L. Rogers	Imperial Chemical Industries
M.A. Tyldesley	Health and Safety Executive

CONTENTS

1. INTRODUCTION

The danger of a dust explosion is difficult to avoid in processes where combustible powders and dusts are handled. Many fine materials, eg coal, wood, flour, starch, sugar, rubber, plastics, some metals, pharmaceuticals, etc can explode once they are dispersed in air as a cloud with a suitable concentration and when an effective ignition source is present.

Dust cloud explosions cause a rapid increase in pressure when confined in vessels or other process equipment. Such pressures cannot be contained by most dust-handling plant and measures have to be taken either to prevent the explosion or to protect the plant against the destructive effects.

One method of explosion protection is known as explosion relief venting, and is the subject of this guide.

Statistics on the frequency and occurrence of fire and explosion incidents reveal the wide range of materials, industries and ignition sources that can be involved. Data on dust explosions reported to the UK Factory Inspectorate are given in Table 1.1 for the years between 1958 and 1979[1].

Under the auspices of the British Materials Handling Board, an analysis of dust explosion and fire incidents in the years 1979–1984 was conducted by the Warren Spring Laboratory[2]. A further analysis for the years 1985–1988 has been added by Porter based on data from the UK Health and Safety Executive[3].

The data shown in Figures 1.1–1.4 (see pages 2–3) are taken from the paper by Porter[3], and divide the known incidents between different types of dust, different types of dust-handling equipment and different types of ignition source. The highest percentage of known incidents takes place in the paper and wood

TABLE 1.1
UK reported explosions (1958–79)

Period	Explosions	Fatal injuries	Non-fatal injuries
1958–1967	247	9	324
1962–1979	474	25*	633

* 10 in 2 incidents

industries, with metals and food products at a somewhat lower percentage. Of the items of dust-handling equipment that could be differentiated, mills, dryers and filters had the largest percentages of known incidents, while of the known ignition sources, friction and mechanical failure, flames and flaming material, and over-heating and spontaneous heating proved to be the most frequent.

German incident data has been analysed by the Berufsgenossenschaftliches Institut für Arbeitssicherheit (BIA)[4,5] and the results summarized by Jeske and Beck[6]. Tables 1.2–1.7 (see pages 4–7) are taken from the paper by Jeske and Beck.

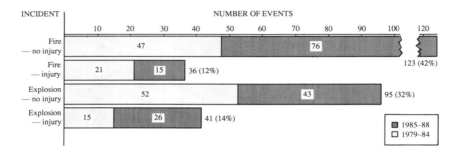

Figure 1.1   HSE (1979–88) — type of event (based on 295 events).

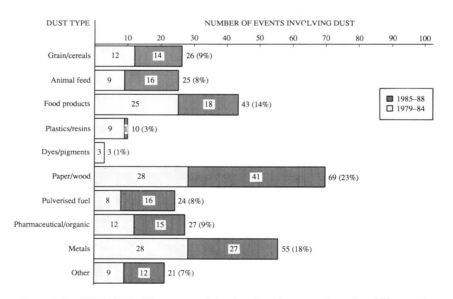

Figure 1.2   HSE (1979–88) — type of dust involved in events (based on 303 events).

2

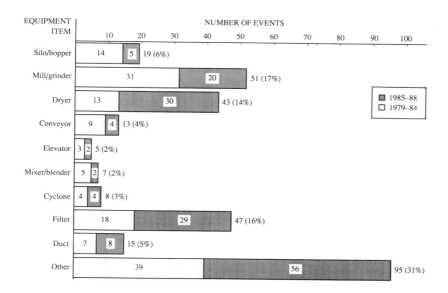

Figure 1.3   HSE (1979–88) — equipment involved in incident (based on 303 events).

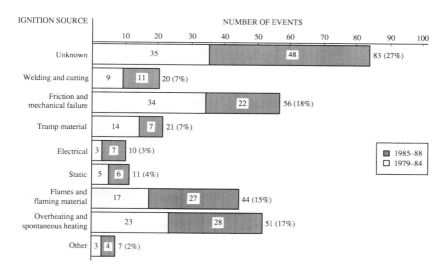

Figure 1.4   HSE (1979–88) — ignition sources of events (based on 303 events).

This data demonstrates that, overall, the highest frequency of explosion incidents occurs in silos/bunkers, extractors/separators and milling machines. However, this frequency changes from industry to industry, with, for example, silos of predominant importance in the wood/wood products industry. Extractors/separators have the highest frequency in the metals industry, but a low frequency in the food and fodder industries.

In agreement with the UK data, mechanical sparks prove to be the most frequent cause of ignition, with smouldering clumps of dust the next most frequent. However, these frequencies are industry dependent: in the plastics industry electrostatic discharges are the most frequent source of ignition.

If combustible, dusty materials are handled there is a statutory requirement (in the UK) to take practicable precautions. These requirements are embodied in the Factories Act 1961. Sub-sections 31(1), (2) and (4) provide as follows:

'(1) Where, in connection with any grinding, sieving, or other process giving rise to dust, there may escape dust of such a character and to such an extent as to be

TABLE 1.2

Proportions of the evaluated dust explosions accounted for by individual plant groups (reproduced by permission of the Berufsgenossenschaftliches Institut für Arbeitssicherheit (BIA))

Plant group	% share
Silos/bunkers	20.2
Dust-extractors/separators	17.2
Milling and reducing units	13.0
Conveying units	10.1
Driers	8.0
Firing plants	5.4
Mixers	4.7
Grinding, polishing and matting machines	4.5
Screening units (sifters)	2.8
Others	14.1

4

TABLE 1.3

Proportions accounted for by individual plant groups within the wood/wood products dust group (reproduced by permission of the Berufsgenossenschaftliches Institut für Arbeitssicherheit (BIA))

Plant group	% share
Silos	35.9
Dust-extractors/separators	18.0
Firing plants	10.9
Driers	10.2
Milling and reducing units	7.0
Conveying units	4.7
Screening units (sifters)	4.7
Grinders	3.9
Others	4.7

TABLE 1.4

Proportions accounted for by individual plant groups within the food and fodder dust group (reproduced by permission of the Berufsgenossenschaftliches Institut für Arbeitssicherheit (BIA))

Plant group	% share
Conveying units (elevators)	26.7
Silos	22.9
Milling units	18.1
Dust-extractors/separators	9.5
Driers	7.6
Screening units	2.8
Firing plants	1.9
Others	10.5

TABLE 1.5
Proportions accounted for by individual plant groups within the metals dust group (reproduced by permission of the Berufsgenossenschaftliches Institut für Arbeitssicherheit (BIA))

Plant group	% share
Dust-extractors/separators	45.6
Grinding, polishing and matting machines	22.8
Milling units	5.3
Mixers	3.5
Screening units	3.5
Others	19.3

TABLE 1.6
Proportions accounted for by individual types of ignition source in the evaluated dust explosions (reproduced by permission of the Berufsgenossenschaftliches Institut für Arbeitssicherheit (BIA))

Plant group	% share
Mechanical sparks	26.1
Smouldering clumps	11.3
Mechanical heating	8.9
Electrostatic discharge	8.7
Fire (conflagration/firing, etc)	7.8
Spontaneous ignition	4.9
Hot surface	4.9
Welding work (flames, sparks, etc)	4.9
Electrical equipment	2.8
Unknown/not determined	16.0
Others	3.5

TABLE 1.7

Proportions accounted for by individual types of ignition source within the plastics dust group (reproduced by permission of the Berufsgenossenschaftliches Institut für Arbeitssicherheit (BIA))

Plant group	% share
Electrostatic discharge	34.6
Mechanical sparks	21.2
Smouldering clumps	9.6
Mechanical heating	9.6
Hot surface	3.9
Unknown/not determined	11.5
Others	9.6

liable to explode on ignition, all practicable steps shall be taken to prevent such an explosion by enclosure of the plant used in the process, and by removal or prevention of accumulation of any dust that may escape in spite of the enclosure, and by exclusion or effective enclosure of possible sources of ignition.

'(2) Where there is present in any plant used in any such process as aforesaid dust of such a character and to such an extent as to be liable to explode on ignition, then, unless the plant is so constructed as to withstand the pressure likely to be produced by any such explosion, all practicable steps shall be taken to restrict the spread and effects of such an explosion by the provision, in connection with the plant, of chokes, baffles and vents, or other equally effective appliances.

'(4) No plant, tank or vessel which contains or has contained any explosive or inflammable substance shall be subjected:

(a) to any welding, brazing or soldering operation;

(b) to any cutting operation which involves the application of heat; or

(c) to any operation involving the application of heat for the purpose of taking apart or removing the plant, tank or vessel or any part of it; until all practicable steps have been taken to remove the substance and any fumes arising from it, or to render them non-explosive or non-inflammable; and if any plant, tank or vessel has been subjected to any such operation, no explosive or inflammable substance shall be allowed to enter the plant, tank or vessel until the metal has cooled sufficiently to prevent any risk of igniting the substance.'

In addition to the above sections of the Factories Act, the Health and Safety at Work Act 1974 imposes general duties on employers and employees. These are intended to ensure, amongst other things, the safety both of those at work and people who may be affected by a work activity.

Clearly these duties will extend to measures intended to control the risk and consequences of dust explosions.

Section 2(2) of the HSW Act specifies that the duties of an employer include in particular 'the provision and maintenance of plant and systems of work that are, so far as is reasonably practicable, safe and without risks to health'.

Where a plant will or may contain a flammable dust, precautions such as those set out in the following pages will be needed to comply with this requirement.

Section 6 of the HSW Act sets out the duties, both of those who design, manufacture, import or supply articles (eg process plant) and those who manufacture, import or supply substances (eg flammable dusts) for use at work.

Specifically the duties include:

(a) 'to ensure, so far as is reasonably practicable, that the article is so designed and constructed that it will be safe and without risks to health at all times when it is being set, used and cleaned or maintained by a person at work';

(b) 'to carry out or arrange for the carrying out of testing . . . ' to comply with (a);

(c) . . . 'to provide adequate information about the use for which the article has been designed or tested . . . '.

Providers of process plant who know that it will be used for handling flammable dusts may need to fit explosion vents, or provide other safety features described in this guide to comply with this section of the Act. Information provided with the plant should indicate the types of material (eg St classification of the flammable dust) which may be handled safely.

Where flammable dusts are provided the duties include:

(a) 'ensuring, so far as is reasonably practicable, that the substance will be safe and without risks to health at all times when it is being used, handled, processed, stored or transported . . . ';

(b) 'carrying out of such testing as may be necessary' . . . to comply with (a);

(c) 'providing adequate information about any risks to health or safety to which the inherent properties of the substance may give rise, about the results of any relevant tests which may have been carried out . . . and about any conditions necessary to ensure that the substance will be safe . . . at all such times as mentioned in (a) above'.

This will involve carrying out tests such as those described in later chapters, on dusts known or suspected to be flammable, or unstable, and providing the results to customers.

This is not intended to be a comprehensive guide to the legislation, and fuller advice is available from the local office of the Health and Safety Executive.

The Health and Safety Executive enforces these legal requirements in most factory premises. Explosion venting is a common precaution against the effects of dust explosions and is widely used in part fulfilment of the legal requirements.

In any case of doubt concerning explosion hazard and precautions in a given process the Health and Safety Executive Inspectors should be consulted in addition to obtaining other expert advice.

A considerable body of literature on dust explosion hazards has been generated in recent years and a great deal of research continues to be done. An extensive list of references is given at the end of the text. Recent books concerned with dust explosions include:

Bartknecht, W., 1981, *Explosions: course, prevention, protection* (Springer-Verlag)[7].

Bartknecht, W., 1989, *Dust explosions: course, prevention, protection* (Springer-Verlag)[8].

Field, P., 1982, *Dust explosions* (Elsevier)[1].

Eckhoff, R.K., 1991, *Dust explosions in the process industries* (Butterworth Heinemann)[9].

Cashdollar, K.L. and Hertzberg, M. (Eds), 1987, *Industrial dust explosions* (ASTM)[10].

Nagy, J. and Verakis, H.C., 1983, *Development and control of dust explosions* (Marcel Dekker)[11].

Guides and codes describing the requirements for protection and prevention include:

Lunn, G.A., 1984, *Venting of gas and dust explosions — a review* (Institution of Chemical Engineers, Rugby, UK)[12].

Schofield, C. and Abbott, J.A., 1988, *Guide to dust explosion prevention and protection. Part 2 — Ignition, inerting, suppression and isolation* (Institution of Chemical Engineers, Rugby, UK)[13].

Lunn, G.A., 1988, *Guide to dust explosion prevention and protection. Part 3 — Venting of weak explosions and the effect of vent ducts* (Institution of Chemical Engineers, Rugby, UK)[14].

Abbott, J.A., 1990, *Prevention of fires and explosions in dryers* (Institution of Chemical Engineers, Rugby, UK)[15].

NFPA, 1988, *Guide for venting of deflagrations (NFPA 68)* (National Fire Protection Association, Quincy, USA)[16].

VDI, 1984, *Pressure release of dust explosions (VDI 3673)* (Verein Deutscher Ingenieure — Kommission Reinhaltung der Luft, Germany)[17].

The first edition of this IChemE guide, *Dust explosion prevention and protection. Part I — Venting*[18], by Dr C. Schofield, was published in 1985.

1.1   USING THE GUIDE/CHAPTER CONTENTS

The guide is a compilation of current best practice in the design of vents for dust explosions.

The various methods for calculating venting requirements are described and discussed in several chapters. The first, in Chapter 4, are called here the basic methods, in that they are the ones currently most widely used. The sizing of relief vents by these basic methods has been shown to protect industrial plant satisfactorily, and these methods are primarily the ones recommended for use by this guide.

Methods which extend the basic methods or make different assumptions concerning either the dust explosibility characteristics or the degree of turbulence in the dust cloud are discussed in later chapters, along with guidance for non-compact enclosures and for some special items of dust-handling plant. Finally, the important aspects of vent closure and vent ducts are discussed, with some insight into the real practical aspects of venting industrial plant. The areas covered by Chapters 2–8 are described below. Worked examples are included where appropriate.

CHAPTER 2 — BACKGROUND TO DUST EXPLOSIONS, PRECAUTIONS AND THE SELECTION OF A BASIS FOR SAFETY

This chapter discusses the general background to dust explosions, the factors that can influence the violence of the explosion, characteristics of the dust that are important to the consideration of explosions and fires and the various methods there are for the prevention of and protection against dust explosions.

The various stages which need to be considered before a decision to use venting is finally made are described by means of text and a series of logic diagrams.

CHAPTER 3 — DETERMINATION OF DUST EXPLOSION CHARACTERISTICS

This chapter describes and discusses the standard methods for measuring important characteristics of the dust which are needed for estimating the venting requirements. These methods are: explosibility testing to assess whether precautions are necessary; measurements of the rate of pressure rise and the maximum explosion pressure in enclosed vessels.

CHAPTER 4 — SIZING OF VENTS — THE BASIC METHODS

This chapter describes and discusses the basic methods for assessing the venting areas of compact enclosures. These methods are the K_{st} nomograph and St nomograph methods, the vent ratio approach and the K factor method. These are the recommended methods. Only when it is either impractical to fit the required vent area, or the process conditions are outside the range of applicability of the basic methods, should other methods be used. The evidence for and reasoning behind a move away from the basic methods must be fully explored.

CHAPTER 5 — EXTENSIONS TO THE BASIC METHODS

The basic methods do not cover every eventuality. The K_{st} nomograph method does not cover low strength equipment for instance. This chapter discusses some methods for assessing the venting requirements of low strength equipment; for example, an extension of the K_{st} nomograph approach and an equation given as guidance in the American NFPA 68.

The basic K_{st} nomographs apply to dusts with high values of the maximum explosion pressure, P_{max}, and a given degree of turbulence. Variations of the nomograph approach have been derived for dusts with lower values of P_{max}, and a method is available for use when very high degrees of turbulence can be expected.

The guidance described in this chapter is not as well-founded as the basic methods, and great care must be exercised in its application. The evidence for using a particular method and the reasoning behind its use must be fully explored.

CHAPTER 6 — SPECIAL METHODS FOR DIFFERENT TYPES OF PLANT, INCLUDING PIPELINES AND SILOS, AND SITUATIONS INVOLVING PNEUMATIC FILLING

The basic methods are not applicable to all types of equipment. This chapter discusses the methods for estimating the venting requirements of dust-carrying pipelines, silos and other items of equipment where extra guidance is available. These include fluid bed units, filters, mills, etc. This chapter also examines some guidance that is available for venting explosions when the turbulence is less than that simulated in the standard explosibility test and when the dust cloud is not as well dispersed in terms of either uniform concentration or filling of the vessel. The discussion is limited to the pneumatic charging of vented vessels, where substantial savings in vent area can be made, but only if conditions are right.

CHAPTER 7 — DESIGN OF VENT CLOSURES AND VENT DUCTING, AND SAFE DISCHARGE AREAS

This chapter discusses the types of vent closure that are available and gives guidance on the effect of vent ducts used to carry the explosion to a safe place. Other topics in this chapter are the venting of buildings containing dust-handling equipment, the safe discharge area for a vented explosion and the calculation of reaction forces.

CHAPTER 8 — EXAMPLES OF EXPLOSION VENTING IN INDUSTRIAL PLANT

This chapter describes some practical aspects of venting dust explosions with examples from real dust-handling facilities.

2. BACKGROUND TO DUST EXPLOSIONS, PRECAUTIONS AND THE SELECTION OF A BASIS FOR SAFETY

A dust explosion can take place if a number of conditions are simultaneously satisfied:

- The dust must be explosible.

- The dust must have a particle size distribution that will allow the propagation of flame.

- The atmosphere into which the dust is dispersed as a cloud or suspension must contain sufficient oxidant to support combustion.

- The dust cloud must have a concentration within the explosible range.

- The dust cloud must be in contact with an ignition source of sufficient energy to cause an ignition.

The hazard from an explosion depends on several factors concerning both the dust and the environment in which it is dispersed:

- The dust itself. Dusts vary in their explosion violence. Coal dust is of a relatively low explosion violence when this is measured in standard tests, less explosible than aspirin and much less explosible than fine aluminium powder.

- The composition of the dust. Some dusts — and coal is a prime example — are not homogeneous and can have very different compositions depending on the source. Coal dust generally has a higher explosion violence the greater the volatile content. Some anthracite is non-explosible because the volatile content is low. Other examples include the variation of fat content in milk and the presence of de-dusting agents.

- The particle size and particle size distribution. The finer the particles the greater the surface area and thus the more explosible a given dust is likely to be. When the dust is made up of a series of particle sizes ranging from fine to coarse, the fines play the most prominent part in an ignition and in the propagation of an explosion.

- The concentration of dispersed dust. When the concentration of dispersed dust is below a certain value, an explosion cannot be propagated. This concentration is the lower explosibility limit (LEL), typically 10–500 g/m^3. The explosion violence of the cloud increases as the dust concentration increases until an optimum concentration is reached giving the highest explosion violence; this concentration is usually well in excess of the amount of dust theoretically required to react with the available oxygen. At higher concentrations still the explosion violence either decreases or stays roughly constant. The upper explosibility limit (UEL) — the dust concentration above which an explosion cannot be propagated — is not as clearly defined as the lower limit. At high concentrations of coal dust, for example, the flame travels rapidly through a reactive volatiles/air mixture as soon as this mixture is produced and leaves the partly devolatilized particles in its wake[19]. Only at very high dust concentrations is the inerting effect of these particles sufficient to quench the flame.

• Moisture content. The explosion violence falls as the moisture content of a dust increases. Eventually the dust is no longer explosible.

• Ambient temperature and pressure. Although at a given dust concentration an increase in the ambient temperature results in a decrease in the maximum explosion pressure in an enclosed explosion, it has very little effect on the rate of pressure rise. If the ambient pressure increases, both the maximum pressure and the rate of pressure rise increase.

• Turbulence of the dust cloud. Dust clouds are usually turbulent to some degree because there must be some air movement if the dust is to remain dispersed. At low levels of turbulence the explosion violence of a dust cloud may be relatively mild, but at high states of turbulence, when the flame front is broken up and its effective area much increased, the explosion will propagate much more rapidly and the explosion violence will reach high values.

• The presence of flammable gas. Admixture of a low concentration of flammable gas can increase the explosion violence of a dispersed dust cloud markedly. These are so called 'hybrid mixtures'.

• The scale of the vessel. The violence of a dust explosion — as indicated by the rate of pressure rise — depends on the size of the vessel. The larger the vessel the slower the rate of pressure rise, although the potential for destruction will be greater because of the increased scale of the explosion. One of the simplest scaling laws is the cubic law which relates the rate of pressure rise in an explosion to the cube root of the vessel volume.

2.1 DUST FIRE AND EXPLOSION CHARACTERISTICS AND PRECAUTIONS AGAINST DUST EXPLOSIONS

Precautions against dust explosions fall into two categories, namely *prevention* and *protection*, and they are summarized in Table 2.1.

Prevention methods aim to ensure that the conditions under which an explosion becomes possible never occur. *Protection* methods aim to minimize the effects of explosions which it is assumed will occur.

TABLE 2.1

Common methods used in controlling dust explosions

Precautionary measure	Comments	Parameter
Inerting (exclusion of oxygen using N_2, CO_2 or other suitable gas).	Reduces oxygen content below minimum necessary to support combustion (typically < 5–15%). Requires monitoring of oxygen content. Usually requires closed system to conserve inert gas.	Limiting oxygen concentration.
Avoidance of ignition sources.	All practical measures must be taken to exclude ignition sources. Because sources are often unknown it is difficult to guarantee their exclusion, so other precautions are usually taken.	Layer ignition temperature. Cloud ignition temperature. Decomposition temperature. Spontaneous ignition temperature. Minimum ignition energy. Electrostatic behaviour.
Detection of smouldering particles (wood flour industry, metal working).	Detection of smouldering particles in pneumatic transport or dust extraction lines by infra-red sensors and quenching by a triggered water spray to reduce the probability of ignition.	
Concentration limitation (exclusion of dust cloud).	Material can be rendered less dusty and the handling system designed to minimize dust, or altered to a wet process.	Lower explosiblity limit.
Replacement of combustible materials (diluent dust addition — to reduce explosibility of dust).	Non-combustible diluent, well mixed with dust, acts as heat sink thus reducing explosibility of dust. Limited application because of contamination.	Combustibility, heat of combustion, explosibility.

Continued on following page

15

TABLE 2.1 (continued)
Common methods used in controlling dust explosions

Precautionary measure	Comments	Parameter
Explosion-resistant construction (containment).	Vessel and associated pipework, etc built sufficiently strong to withstand the maximum explosion pressure.	Maximum explosion pressure
Isolation.	Ensuring explosions cannot propagate between items of plant, eg rotary valves, fast-acting cut-off valves and extinguishing barriers.	Maximum rate of pressure rise and maximum explosion pressure. Flame speed.
Explosion pressure relief (venting).	Vents provided in walls of vessel to allow escape of dust and combustion products to limit pressure rise to an acceptable level. Widely used.	Maximum rate of pressure rise and maximum explosion pressure.
Explosion suppression.	Start of explosion detected by instruments which trigger release of fire suppressants. Useful where venting is unacceptable or impracticable, eg when the dust is toxic.	Maximum rate of pressure rise and maximum explosion pressure. Cloud ignition temperature.

Generally, the practical approach to dust explosion precautions takes the following route:

• Where possible select less dusty alternatives for materials and minimize attrition.

• Minimize handling of dusty materials and design handling system to minimize dust generation and the size of dust clouds.

• Avoid the accumulation of dust (which can be disturbed to form a dust cloud) by the detailed design of equipment, building and working practices.

• Anticipate possible ignition sources and eliminate them, as far as is reasonably practicable, by appropriate equipment design, earthing, maintenance and working practices.

• Take appropriate additional precautions, where practicable, such as inerting, containment, venting or suppression.

• Isolate plant vulnerable to explosion risk as appropriate.

Important dust fire and explosion characteristics are measured in standard tests and are essential to the application of precautionary measures. These characteristics are listed in Table 2.1 alongside the precautionary measures for which they are important. Some examples of recorded values are given in Table 2.2 on page 18.

The characteristics which apply to methods for the *prevention* of dust explosions are:

• The explosibility limits — the dust cloud concentrations which define the lower and upper values to the range of concentrations over which an explosion can occur.

Exclusion of an explosible dust cloud is one prevention method.

• The minimum ignition energy — the electrical energy necessary to ignite a dust cloud. Values range from about 1 mJ to above 10^4 mJ[20].

• The minimum ignition temperature — the minimum temperature of a standard furnace apparatus that will cause the ignition of a dust cloud[21].

• The layer ignition temperature (sometimes referred to as glow temperature) — the temperature of a hot surface necessary to ignite a dust layer. In the standard test the layer is 5 mm thick, but in practice the layer depth can strongly influence the layer ignition temperature; the thicker the layer the lower the layer ignition temperature. The layer ignition temperature cannot be divorced from an induction time, defined as the time between initial heating and onset of glowing. The standard test is limited to a period of 2 hours[21]. Consideration has to be given to the actual practical situation, and other tests have been developed for measuring the limiting temperatures for exothermic reaction under differing conditions[15].

The exclusion of all obvious ignition sources capable of igniting dust clouds is normally the first step in safety rather than a basis for safety. Total elimination of all sources is difficult to guarantee. The possibility of self-ignition must also be excluded.

Important ignition sources that should be excluded as far as possible no matter what other precautions are taken include hot surfaces, electrical and mechanically generated sparks, static electricity, flames and spontaneous ignition of dust deposits.

• Limiting oxygen concentration — the concentration of oxygen in a mixture of oxygen and inert gas or gases which will just fail to support a dust explosion. The limiting oxygen concentration depends on the dust and the inert gas: typical values when nitrogen is the inert gas range from 5–15%[20].

Limiting the oxygen concentration by feeding in inert gases — a technique known as inerting — is a highly effective method of preventing dust explosions if circumstances favour its application.

TABLE 2.2
Explosibility parameters for a number of dusts*

Type of dust	Min. cloud ignition energy, mJ	Ignition temp. Cloud °C	Layer °C	Max. explosion press., bar a	Max. rate of press. rise**, bar/s	Min. explosible conc., g/m³	Limiting O₂ conc., vol %
Pea flour	40	560	260	–	–	–	15
Lignite	30	390	180	11.0	151	60	12
Aluminium	15	550	740	13.0	750	60	5
Coal	60	610	170	9.8	114	15	14
Cellulose	80	480	270	11.0	125	30	9
Cornflour	40	380	330	10.3	125	60	9
Wood	40	470	260	10.2	142	60	10
Wheat flour	50	380	360	9.8	70	125	11
Charcoal	20	530	180	10.0	10	60	–
Cotton linter	1920	560	350	8.2	24	100	–
Skimmed milk	50	490	200	9.8	125	60	–
Sugar	30	370	400	9.5	138	60	–
Lamp black	–	730	520	10.2	85	60	–
Sulphur	15	190	220	7.8	151	30	–
Magnesium	80	450	240	18.5	508	30	–
Zinc	9600	690	540	7.8	93	250	–
Paraform-aldehyde	–	460	> 480	10.9	178	60	6

* Examples of recorded values. For information only: not to be used in the calculations for explosion precaution methods.

** 1m³ vessel

Protection methods are based on measurements of dust explosibility. This is determined in standard tests which measure the maximum explosion pressure and maximum rate of pressure rise. These tests will be described and discussed in Chapter 3.

There are several techniques available to curtail the destructive effects of an explosion. They should be used in conjunction with appropriate prevention methods if it is deemed necessary. In some circumstances, however, prevention techniques based on the exclusion of flammable atmospheres or ignition sources can be used alone if they provide a satisfactory basis for safety.

● Containment — the vessel is strong enough to withstand the pressure of a confined explosion. *Explosion pressure resistant* plant can withstand the explosion pressure of a confined explosion several times without permanent deformation. *Explosion pressure shock resistant* plant can withstand the explosion pressure of a confined explosion without rupture but with some permanent deformation[20]. If plant is operated at pressures well below atmospheric either the explosion will not be supported because the pressure is too low, or the maximum explosion pressure will not reach 1 bar a, eg if the operating pressure is 0.1 bar a then dusts with maximum explosion pressures of less than 10 bar will remain confined in the plant[20].

● Isolation — explosions must be isolated from other parts of dust-handling plant if the destructive effects are to be limited. Rotary valves, fast-acting valves, extinguishing barriers and explosion diverters are some of the methods for doing this[13].

● Suppression — injecting suppressant material into an explosion as soon as possible after ignition[13]. Explosion pressures are thus kept low.

● Venting — a technique whereby weak panels open in the walls of a plant early in the development of the explosion. The main force of the explosion is dissipated in the open air.

References 13, 14, 15, 16 and 20 give detailed guidance on dust explosion safety measures. Their correct application relies on a thorough knowledge of the plant, the dust and the dust-handling process.

Section 2.2 discusses the process of defining an overall basis for safety with regard to the dust explosion hazard. The section consists of a number of decision trees, with accompanying notes, which lead the reader through the various stages that establish whether or not the dust is explosible and which is the most appropriate solution among the safety options available.

There is no 'best' technique when it comes to taking precautions against dust explosions. Each piece of plant or part of a process must be assessed separately and then appropriate precautions taken with due consideration of the effect that an explosion might have on other items of plant or other parts of the process. Some thought must be given to the approach given in Section 2.1 which considers how the dangers of and damage from a dust explosion can be minimized. It is not sufficient, for example, merely to install a protection technique such as venting without having first done all that is practicable to prevent an explosion by such means as exclusion of ignition sources.

2.2 SELECTION OF A BASIS FOR SAFETY

A basis for safety is defined as an explanation of why the plant is safe followed by a list of the precautions taken.

Figure 2.1 is a logic diagram which describes the overall process of defining a basis for safety for handling flammable dusts.

The first step taken in defining a basis for safety is to conduct a screening procedure that will identify powders with the properties of explosives. Materials exhibiting explosive properties are not manufactured in general chemical plant, and are not covered in this guide. This screening procedure is described in the IChemE guide, *Prevention of fires and explosions in dryers*[15].

An explosive material is one that rapidly decomposes with the evolution of large amounts of energy and large volumes of gas. The decomposition often involves the oxygen contained in the molecule. Three factors must be considered:

• The chemical composition of the material — the influence of groups in the molecule can modify the behaviour markedly.

• The oxygen balance of organic molecules — the availability of oxygen often indicates the explosive potential of the material and the oxygen balance enables the availability of oxygen to be compared with known explosives. In the calculation of the oxygen balance only carbon, hydrogen and oxygen are taken to be involved, ie

$$C_xH_yO_z + (x + y/4 - z/2)O_2 \rightarrow xCO_2 + y/2\ H_2O$$

and the oxygen balance is

$$\frac{-16\ (2x + y/2 - z) \times 100}{\text{Molecular weight}}$$

• The reactions of the material in standard flammability tests — material must be submitted for testing for explosive properties if the material structure suggests it may be explosive and if the oxygen balance is more positive than −200.

There are various stages to be gone through in order to establish whether or not a dust is explosible, and to establish the best solution among the

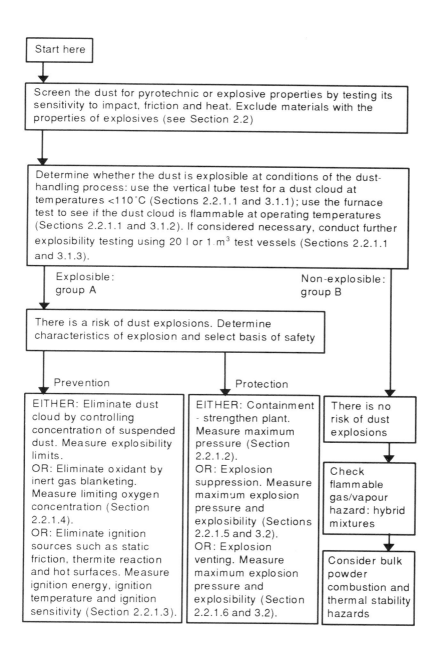

Figure 2.1   Evaluation of dust explosion hazard and options available for basis of safety.

options available for precautionary methods. These have been put in the form of a series of logic diagrams or decision trees, starting at Figure 2.2 with an assessment of the capability of a dust to take part in an explosion.

Depending on the results of an explosibility test and consideration of process conditions such as temperature, dust concentration, state of the dust and whether flammable vapours are present a conclusion is reached as to whether an explosibility hazard exists or not. If it is decided that a hazard exists, there are a number of options on which a basis for safety could rest. Each of these options has its own logic diagram, Figures 2.3–2.7, and these take the reader through the decisions that are necessary before either the option can be accepted or another option considered. The logic diagram for exclusion of ignition sources is a special case; every attempt to exclude ignition sources must be made even if at the end further precautions are considered necessary. As this logic diagram makes clear, using exclusion of ignition sources as the sole precautionary method requires particular care needing formalized operating procedures and operator training.

Explanatory notes relating to the logic diagrams are given with each diagram.

2.2.1 EXPLANATORY NOTES RELATING TO LOGIC DIAGRAMS

These explanatory notes refer to the logic diagrams in Figures 2.2 to 2.7. The bracketed numbers relate to those on the logic diagrams.

2.2.1.1 LOGIC DIAGRAM FOR TESTING AND DESIGN (FIGURE 2.2)

Tests for dust explosibility define whether a hazard exists. Measurements of the lower explosibility limit are important with regard to the dust concentration.

(1) EXPLOSIBILITY TESTING

Satisfactory designs to control dust explosion hazards must always be based on the results of tests performed on the materials involved in the process concerned. If material is unavailable for testing, then it must be considered explosible and sensitive to ignition unless there is evidence to the contrary.

Dusts are considered to be Group A if they ignite and propagate flame in approved test apparatus such as the vertical tube at ambient conditions. If there is no flame propagation, the dust is considered to be Group B.

(2) RETEST/SIEVING AND DRYING

Often tests are done on samples as received. If the sample does not ignite it should be retested under conditions of dryness and fineness appropriate to the

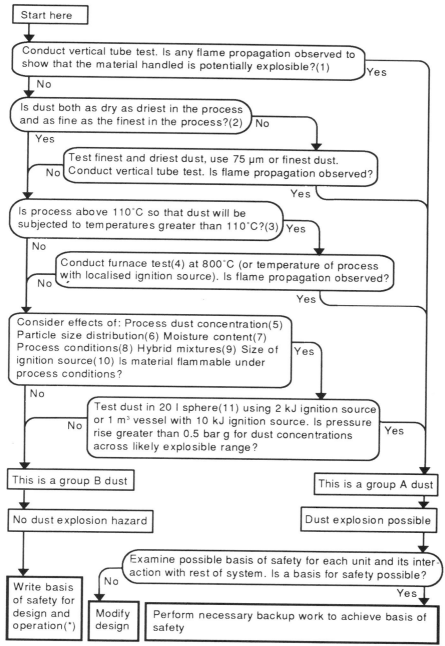

Figure 2.2   Logic diagram for testing and design.
*   Formal definition of basis of safety — All practicable steps should be taken to avoid hazards. It is, therefore, strongly recommended that the basis of safety for the design should be formally recorded.

process. Materials classified as Group B at ambient temperature may be explosible when process temperatures are higher than ambient, or larger ignition sources are potentially present.

(3) RETEST AT PROCESS TEMPERATURE

A process temperature of 110°C is usually considered to be the temperature above which further testing of the likelihood of explosibility is considered necessary. Such a test is desirable in order to assess explosibility and sensitivity to ignition sources in heated environments.

(4) TEST AT ELEVATED TEMPERATURE

Although there is no nationally accepted test, the effect of elevated temperature is usually tested in the Godbert-Greenwald furnace set at a temperature of 800°C. This is a rigorous test for explosibility on account of the high temperature and large ignition source. If flame propagation is observed the dust is re-classified as Group A. This result can be accepted as the final assessment but because of the test's severity, further testing may be necessary to take into account less severe process conditions. This can be done by performing the furnace test at the known temperature of the process and with a localized ignition source inside the furnace tube. If flame propagation is observed the dust is classified as Group A.

Dusts which remain classified as Group B may require further testing in the 20 litre or 1 m^3 test vessels. (See (10) and (11).)

(5) EFFECT OF PROCESS DUST CONCENTRATION ON EXPLOSIBILITY CLASSIFICATION

When the concentration of dispersed dust is below a certain value, an explosion cannot be propagated. This concentration is the lower explosibility limit (LEL), typically 10–500 g/m^3. The explosion violence of the cloud increases as the dust concentration increases until an optimum concentration is reached giving the highest explosion violence; this concentration is usually well in excess of the amount of dust theoretically required to react with the available oxygen. At higher concentrations still the explosion violence either decreases or stays roughly constant. The upper explosibility limit (UEL) — the dust concentration above which an explosion cannot be propagated — is not as clearly defined as the lower limit. At high concentrations of coal dust, for example, the flame travels rapidly through a reactive volatiles/air mixture as soon as this mixture is produced and leaves the partly devolatilized particles in its wake[19]. Only at very high dust concentrations is the inerting effect of these particles sufficient to quench the flame.

24

Exclusion of an explosible dust cloud is one prevention method, but it is difficult, in practice, to prevent the formation of a hazardous dust cloud, although choice of plant can do much to minimize the problem. If the dust concentration normally exceeds the upper explosibility limit there will still be times — starting up, shutting down or in the event of a breakdown — when the concentration will be in the explosible range. It is difficult to maintain the necessary high dust concentration, except possibly in dense phase pneumatic transfer operations. Safety can be achieved by operating at concentrations below the LEL[8], for instance in certain extraction ducts of powder/air conveying systems where only a small concentration of explosible dust is present.

Nevertheless it is difficult to guarantee that the dust concentration will always remain below the lower explosibility limit. Dust particles readily settle out as layers that can then be easily dispersed by flow disturbances, producing a cloud with a concentration that will more than likely exceed the lower explosibility limit. Secondary explosions are a case in point: an explosion of a relatively small dust cloud can produce sufficient air movement to disperse dust which then fuels the flame and leads to extensive explosions causing much damage.

Dust dispersion in dust-handling plant is not homogeneous. Dividing the known amount of dust by the known volume is unlikely to give a true value of the dust concentration at any point in the vessel. Operating at a mean concentration below the LEL can be useful but this can only assist other precautionary methods rather than being the sole one.

An increase in temperature decreases the LEL, the effect being the greater the higher the concentration of the room temperature LEL.

(6)   EFFECT OF PARTICLE SIZE/DISTRIBUTION ON EXPLOSIBILITY
         AND SENSITIVITY TO IGNITION

The finer the particles the greater the surface area and thus the more explosible a given dust is likely to be. When the dust is made up of a series of particle sizes ranging from fine to coarse, the fines play the most prominent part in an ignition and in the propagation of an explosion; the effect of the coarse particles on the explosion violence is not significant unless the fraction of coarse particles is high. Fine particles are more readily dispersible and stay in suspension longer but can agglomerate in some circumstances, depending on the dust and the forces attempting to disperse it. Careful consideration sometimes has to be given to what might be the effective particle size in an explosion.

Particles greater than about 500 diameter are unlikely to cause dust explosions, although the possibility of coarser materials producing fine dust by attrition during handling must be anticipated.

For material that can form dust clouds, a Group B classification can only be given after testing a sieved and dried sample. If the material contains both fine and coarse particles, then explosibility tests should be done on a sample that has a particle size less than 75 μm or the finest dust likely to be present in practice. An explosion can be propagated by fine material even when it constitutes only a percentage of the total material in the cloud.

Particle size does not have a marked effect on the LEL. There are no means of precisely predicting the effect of particle size and/or distribution on explosibility and work in this area would be both long-term and expensive to provide a general solution. Acceptance as a basis for safety would also require plant control to maintain the specified distribution. In processes where the particle size distribution can be closely defined, explosibility testing to determine the sensitivity under process conditions can be carried out on representative samples having the size distribution existing in the process.

(7)   EFFECT OF MOISTURE CONTENT ON EXPLOSIBILITY

The explosion violence falls as the moisture content of a dust increases. Eventually the dust is no longer explosible.

Guidelines for the effect of moisture content are as follows:

0–5%: little effect;

5–10%: decrease in sensitivity;

> 25%: the dust is unlikely to be held in suspension and even if it is there will be a further decrease in sensitivity.

To avoid the sample being classified unrealistically, it is important that tests are not carried out on overdried materials, ie on samples containing less than the minimum moisture content found under normal process conditions.

In processes where the minimum moisture content can be closely defined, explosibility testing to determine the sensitivity under process conditions should be carried out using a sample containing the minimum moisture content found in the process.

(8)   EFFECT OF PROCESS CONDITIONS ON EXPLOSIBILITY

The process conditions which can affect the situation are pressure, temperature and inventory. Consideration should be given to the explosibility of a cloud and the violence of an explosion.

Although at a given dust concentration an increase in the ambient temperature results in a decrease in the maximum explosion pressure in an enclosed explosion, it has very little effect on the rate of pressure rise. If the ambient pressure increases, both the maximum pressure and the rate of pressure rise increase.

(8.1)   PRESSURE

Up to the pressures normally used, namely 2–3 bar g, there is no significant effect.

(8.2)   TEMPERATURE

It is generally considered that a dust classified as Group B at ambient temperatures will remain non-explosible unless the temperature is greater than 110°C.

(8.3)   DUST INVENTORY

The dust inventory has no effect on explosibility of a dust cloud for a given concentration, but can have a marked effect on the self-heating of bulk material.

(9)   EFFECT OF HYBRID MIXTURES (MORE THAN ONE PHASE) ON EXPLOSIBILITY

The presence of flammable gas or vapour as an admixture of low concentration can increase the explosion violence of a dispersed dust cloud markedly. These are so called 'hybrid mixtures'.

A mixture containing a flammable gas or vapour and an explosible dust may be more explosible than the explosibility characteristics of the individual components might suggest. If both the gas and dust in such a mixture are present in concentrations less than their individual LELs, the mixture may still be explosible. At present, no method exists for predicting limits for such mixtures from theoretical considerations but some experimental data has been published[22,23]. Such mixtures, if necessary, need to be tested using standard methods.

The admixture of a small quantity of flammable gas to a dust cloud can reduce the lower explosibility limit, reduce markedly the minimum ignition energy, decrease the dust concentration at which the highest values of explosibility occur and increase markedly the rate of pressure rise in an enclosed explosion of carbonaceous dusts with weak values of explosibility.

(10)   SIZE OF POTENTIAL IGNITION SOURCES

The localized ignition source used in the vertical tube test may not adequately simulate the potential ignition sources in the real process. The larger the ignition source the greater the probability of a dust being explosible.

(11)   FURTHER TESTING IN 20 LITRE OR 1 M^3 VESSELS

Further testing can be done using either a 20 litre test vessel using an ignition source of energy 0.5 kJ–2.0 kJ or a 1 m^3 vessel with a 10 kJ ignition source.

If a pressure rise of less than 0.5 bar is recorded for all dust concentrations across the likely explosible range, the dust is considered to be non-explosible.

27

2.2.1.2   LOGIC DIAGRAM FOR CONTAINMENT (FIGURE 2.3)

Measurement of a maximum explosion pressure (P_{max}) in a totally confined vessel is relevant to explosion protection by containment.

(12)   CONTAINMENT — GUIDELINES FOR ASSESSMENT

Containment is of possible use for toxic materials where hazard quantification indicates that an emission could present an unacceptable risk. Containment is often used as a measure for protection of plant operating at sub-atmospheric pressures, eg vacuum dryers.

Containment may still be a valid option even if emission of material does not present an unacceptable risk.

Containment is often a suitable option for mills which can be built strong enough to withstand maximum explosion pressures. Due consideration must be given to preventing flame propagation into adjacent equipment.

(13)   CONFIGURATION OF PLANT

If the system consists of several connected items of plant consideration must be given to isolating the various units to prevent transmission of flame or other ignition sources.

Possible isolation devices often used are as follows: (a) rotary valves; (b) ganged slide valve combinations; (c) suitably designed screw feeders with no free volume and where compaction of powder impedes pressure transmission.

Before any of these are used, the ability to withstand the pressure and to prevent transmission of flame, burning particles or blast pressure must be checked.

(14)   CONTAINMENT — ASSESSMENT OF PRESSURE EFFECTS

With multi-volumes or long ducts, pressure piling effects can occur leading to pressure ratios in excess of 10. With simple configurations, maximum pressures can be estimated but with more complex ones this is not possible.

In single vessels, depending on the process conditions, the maximum pressures produced from dust explosions are in the range 7–10 times the operating pressure. The maximum explosion pressure, P_{max}, can be measured in standard tests.

(15)   DISTORTION OF THE VESSEL

In some processes it may not be necessary to prevent vessel deformation during an explosion.

In some applications the vessel is designed to withstand the maximum explosion pressure, P_{max}, without rupture. The maximum pressure measured in

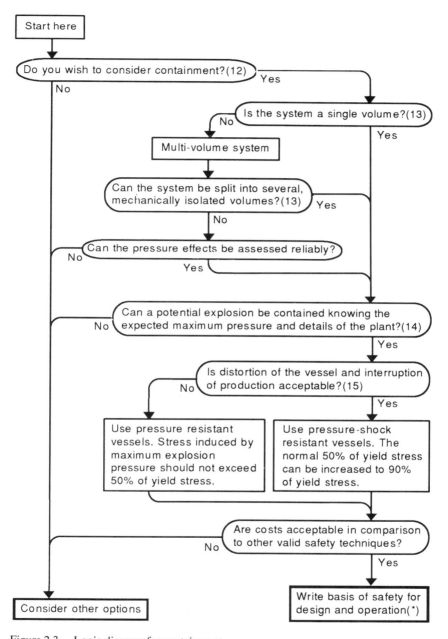

Figure 2.3   Logic diagram for containment.
*   Formal definition of basis of safety — All practicable steps should be taken to
avoid hazards. It is, therefore, strongly recommended that the basis of safety for the
design should be formally recorded.

the small-scale tests can be used, because of its insensitivity to vessel size, to estimate directly the maximum explosion pressure in the vessel.

• Pressure resistant vessels are designed to contain an explosion without rupture or deformation. The stress induced by the maximum explosion pressure should therefore not exceed 50% of the yield stress of the weakest part of the vessel or any attachment. It is recommended that yield stress = 1.5 design stress[8].

• Pressure shock resistant vessels are designed to withstand the maximum explosion pressure but are liable to permanent deformation. The stresses induced by the maximum explosion pressure should not exceed 90% of the yield stress of the weakest part of the vessel or any attachment. It is recommended that yield stress = design stress[8]. But there is still a substantial safety margin up to the ultimate tensile strength.

In some small enclosures the maximum explosion pressure is reduced below that measured in standard tests because of the large internal areas provided by components, eg mills. In others the process entry and exit ports may provide a satisfactory amount of venting, although due consideration must be paid to preventing the propagation of an explosion into other items of plant and other parts of the process. With full information as to how the maximum explosion pressure is limited by internal components and on the enclosure's inherent venting it may be that small vessels especially can be designed so that no extra venting is required. A convincing case would need to be made, and the justification for this option would need to be well documented.

When a vessel is not designed to pressure vessel codes, the difficulty of estimating its strength should not be underestimated. It is the strength of the weakest part of the vessel that must be known, be it weld, join, junction, etc and this determines the explosion pressure which the vessel can withstand.

Quantifying the strength of weak plant, especially when it is old and has been in service for some time, is not easy.

2.2.1.3   LOGIC DIAGRAM FOR EXCLUSION OF IGNITION SOURCES
          (FIGURE 2.4 — see pages 32 and 33)
Minimum ignition energy, minimum ignition temperature and the layer ignition temperature (glow temperature) are important measurements relevant to the avoidance of ignition sources.

(16)   PRESENCE OF IGNITION SOURCES
A thorough study of the plant and the process will indicate the potential ignition sources.

(17)   CONNECTED EQUIPMENT

Incidents have occurred where dust explosions have been attributed to smouldering material. Potential risks from smouldering material can be reduced by:

● Methods of isolation — slam-shut valves activated by ignition detectors;

● Methods of interlocking — power isolation from fans, conveyors, rotary valves, etc.

(18)   HOT SURFACES

Hot surface ignition is related to surface temperature and geometry, contact time, contamination and the chemistry and history of the material on it. Good housekeeping can minimize the risks; preventing the build-up of dust layers on hot surfaces is important.

In the standard test the layer is 5 mm thick, but layer thickness can influence strongly the layer ignition temperature or glow temperature. The thicker the layer the lower the layer ignition temperature. The decrease is approximately 5°C/mm of layer thickness. If the air above the layer is at a temperature higher than normal room temperature, the layer ignition temperature will fall.

A typical decrease is 40°C–60°C at an air temperature of 100°C, but it is preferable to check this by measurement, especially for dryers, where hot air flows are passed over layers by design or pass over layers deposited on internal surfaces in normal running.

The IChemE guide, *Prevention of fires and explosions in dryers*[15], describes tests developed by Gibson, Harper and Rogers which simulate conditions in various types of dryers and obtain measurements of the temperature at which exothermic reaction begins.

The aerated powder test simulates conditions in dryers where a hot air stream passes through material. The powder is held in an 80 mm long, 50 mm diameter glass cylinder closed at each end by sintered glass. Air is passed downwards through the powder at the same temperature as the surroundings inside the fan-assisted oven in which the test is performed. A screening test may be performed, but a more thorough study is made with isothermal tests at different temperatures and for periods exceeding the drying time. The number of isothermal tests will depend on the precision required in the result.

Impurities, slight changes in composition and autocatalytic reactions can have a marked effect on the temperature at which exothermic activity begins. Performing the test with a temperature cycle akin to that likely to occur in the dryer is a useful addition to the isothermal tests. In order to minimize the hazard, a material temperature 30–50°C below the measured temperature is generally recommended, but this safety factor should not be the only basis for safety.

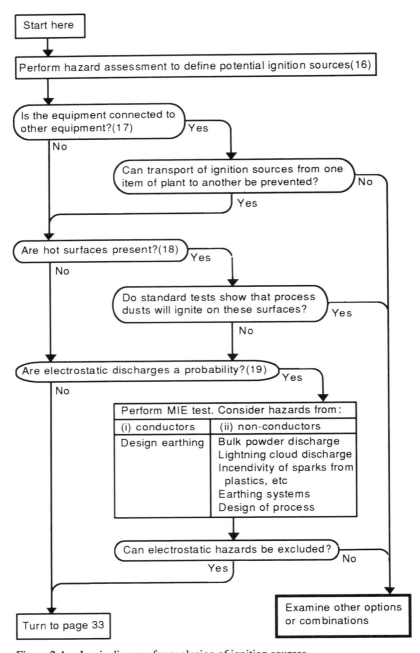

Figure 2.4   Logic diagram for exclusion of ignition sources.
*   Formal definition of basis of safety — All practicable steps should be taken to avoid hazards. It is, therefore, strongly recommended that the basis of safety for the design should be formally recorded.

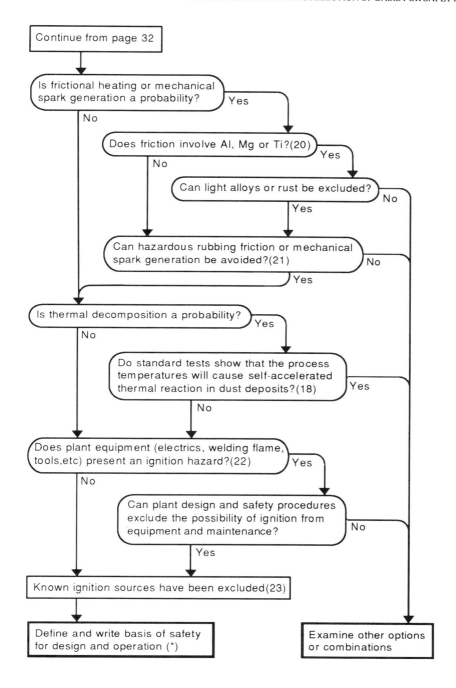

A layer test for dryers where hot air passes over deposits or layers uses a layer 75 mm × 40 mm and 15 mm deep. A screening test can be used, but isothermal tests, each lasting perhaps for several hours, are the main tests by which an ignition temperature is obtained. If the layer depth properly simulates the dryer conditions, the temperature at which an exotherm can progress to red heat can be used as a basis for safe procedures rather than the somewhat lower temperature at which exothermic activity begins. An adequate safety margin is usually 20°C.

A bulk powder test developed by Gibson, Harper and Rogers utilizes the same apparatus as for the aerated powder test but the hot air flows around the sample and not through it. Screening tests, isothermal tests, low heat loss tests and simulation of process cycles can be performed. If the operating temperature is 50°C less than the measured exotherm onset temperature from the screening tests, dangerous decomposition is unlikely to occur at least up to 1 tonne capacity. However, if this temperature difference is less than 50°C, or the operating cycle is longer than the test duration, or the measured temperature is less than 200°C, isothermal tests should be performed at 50°C above the process temperature and with a duration longer than the operational time, followed by a low heat loss test using a Dewar flask.

The build-up of bulk powder at the base of dryers should be prevented, possibly by use of a level detector.

The maximum safe discharge temperatures from dryers are governed by the temperature measured in tests that assess the capability of bulk powders to undergo thermal decomposition. Bulking can occur in cyclones, filters and packages.

If these tests reveal that time, bulk or rate of heat loss are important factors, tests with simulated process conditions should be carried out.

Higher than normal temperatures in the dryer cycle should be minimized, eg at start-up or shut-down. Disturbance of a smouldering dust layer can cause inflammation and so create an ignition source for a dust cloud. Oil soaked layers have markedly reduced ignition temperatures.

The minimum ignition temperature of a dust cloud (MIT) gives a measurement of the surface temperature at which a dust cloud can be ignited. Ignition must be anticipated if surface temperatures higher than the MIT are known to be present. Usually a safety factor of 50°C is adequate, eg the inlet temperature of a dryer.

In areas outside plant which are liable to contamination with combustible dusts, surface temperatures must not exceed a temperature 75°C below the measured ignition temperature of a 5 mm thick layer, and should not exceed ⅔ of the ignition temperature of a dust suspension.

(19)   ELECTROSTATIC DISCHARGES

Detailed guidance on this is given by British Standard BS 5958[25].

The minimum ignition energy measures the ease of ignition by electrical and electrostatic discharges. Particle size has a marked effect on the sensitivity to ignition. The sensitivity to ignition increases with decreasing particle size. There is no means of precisely predicting the effect of particle size and/or distribution. Acceptance as a basis for safety would also require plant control to maintain the specified distribution. In processes where the particle size distribution can be closely defined, testing to determine the ignition sensitivity under process conditions can be carried out on representative samples having the size distribution existing in the process.

Guidelines for the effect of moisture content on the sensitivity to ignition are as follows:

0–5%: little effect;

5–10%: decrease in sensitivity;

> 25%: the dust is unlikely to be held in suspension and even if it is there will be a further decrease in sensitivity.

To avoid the sample being classified as unrealistically sensitive, it is important that tests are not carried out on overdried materials, ie, on samples containing less than the minimum moisture content found under normal process conditions. In processes where the minimum moisture content can be closely defined, testing to determine the ignition sensitivity under process conditions should be carried out using a sample containing the minimum moisture content found in the process. There is no available method for predicting the effect of moisture content on ignition sensitivity.

The sensitivity to ignition of an explosible dust can be markedly affected by relatively small increases in temperature. The MIE value can decrease by a factor of 10 for a temperature change from 20–100°C [8,26].

The major hazard from static electricity is a spark from a conductor and this can be eliminated by earthing plant and personnel. In a small but significant number of incidents the cause has been attributed to static electricity despite the earthing of all conductors. In assessing electrostatic hazards present in metal plants, when handling sensitive dusts with minimum ignition energies less than 25 mJ, the possibility must be considered of incendive discharges from electrostatically charged non-conducting liquid surfaces, bulk powder, dispersed dust clouds and droplet mists and non-conducting plastics. The degree of risk and extent of safety measures additional to earthing that will be required depend very much on process conditions, plant design and material sensitivity to ignition. For powders having resistivities > 10^{10} ohm.m, such as plastic powders, or when the powder can be completely insulated from earth, eg plastic containers, the problem of static charge generation is likely to be exacerbated.

Process personnel should be earthed by means of appropriate footwear and floors when the MIE of the powder is less than 100 millijoules.

From experience in well designed plants, having only conducting parts, which are grounded and bonded well, and have no internally coated surfaces, explosions due to electrostatic only seem to occur with products with a MIE less than 25 mJ.

A mixture containing a flammable gas and an explosible dust may be more sensitive to ignition than the characteristics of the individual components might suggest. Such mixtures need to be tested using standard methods. In general, flammable gases have very much lower minimum ignition energies than dusts and are of the order of 0.1–1.0 millijoules. Ignition is, therefore, much more likely to occur when a dust cloud exists in the presence of a flammable gas.

The admixture of a small quantity of flammable gas or vapour to a dust cloud can reduce markedly the minimum ignition energy.

The auto-ignition temperature (AIT) of a solvent vapour/air mixture is measured in a standard test. Usually it exceeds 200°C, but not always, and in large vessels ignition may occur at temperatures lower than the measured AIT. Usually a safety factor of 50°C is adequate.

In considering charge on non-conductors as a source of electrostatic ignition, the following points are relevant:

• Lightning type discharges. These are extremely rare within dust clouds and are unlikely to be incendive inside small volumes; for example, in drums.

• Sparks from plastic surfaces. A charge stored on the surface of an insulator (eg plastic) can be released as an incendive spark.

• Earthing systems. A resistance to earth of < 10 megohms is sufficient to earth any metallic conductor. However, tests are usually based on achieving < 10 ohms to earth.

(20)   THERMITE IGNITION

Many of the Group A dusts can be ignited by the thermite reaction. The normal requirements for a thermite ignition by impact are: (a) a light alloy containing, for example, aluminium or titanium is used; (b) rust is present; (c) impact occurs. All three must occur simultaneously for ignition to occur, so one or more must be excluded.

(21)   RUBBING FRICTION AND MECHANICAL SPARKS

This has been implicated as the ignition source in 25% of dust explosions. Tramp metal, hot bearings, moving vanes and belts are the most common sources of ignition. Little work has been done but sufficient evidence exists to indicate that frictional ignition cannot be ignored. It is also a complex area in that friction probably decomposes the material involved and its decomposition products then ignite.

(22)   ELECTRICAL REGULATIONS
The British Standard for use of electrical equipment in dusty areas is BS 6467 Parts I and II[27].

(23)   EXCLUSION OF IGNITION SOURCES AS A BASIS OF SAFETY
Total elimination of all sources is difficult to guarantee. The possibility of self-ignition must also be excluded. This technique is only satisfactory where all ignition sources have been identified and eliminated. Careful analysis of all aspects of design, operation and product reactivity are essential before safety is based solely on exclusion of all possible ignition sources.

The exclusion of all obvious ignition sources is normally the first step in safety rather than a basis for safety.

Important ignition sources that should be excluded as far as possible no matter what other precautions are taken include hot surfaces, electrical and mechanically generated sparks, static electricity, flames and spontaneous ignition of dust deposits.

2.2.1.4   LOGIC DIAGRAM FOR INERTING (FIGURE 2.5 — see page 38)
The limiting oxygen concentration is the important measurement for application of inerting.

(24)   LIMITING THE OXYGEN CONCENTRATION
Limiting the oxygen concentration by feeding in inert gases is a highly effective method of preventing dust explosions if circumstances favour its application. Inerting is only suitable when the system is either closed or well confined; it can be expensive both on initial outlay for equipment and monitoring devices and on running costs, depending on the leakage rate from the plant. Reliable monitoring of the oxygen concentration at various points in the plant is crucial, with trustworthy alarm and shut-down procedures.

(25)   DESIGN DUST INERTING SYSTEM
70–80% inert dust is required for dust inerting to be effective.

(26)   DESIGN GAS INERTING SYSTEM
The minimum oxygen concentration for a given flammable dust/air system varies with the particular inert gas used. When the standard test was carried out

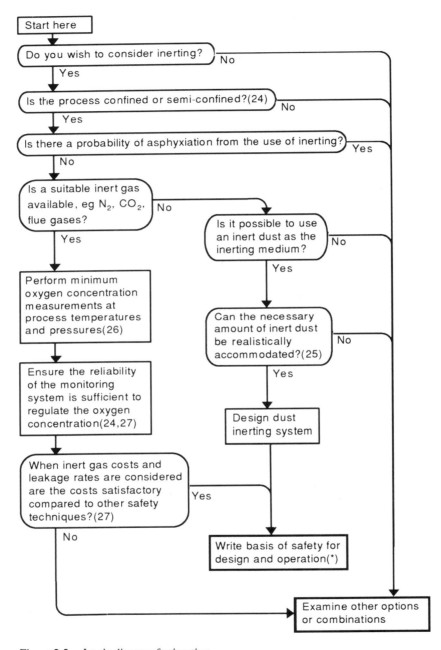

Figure 2.5   Logic diagram for inerting.
*   Formal definition of basis of safety — All practicable steps should be taken to avoid hazards. It is, therefore, strongly recommended that the basis of safety for the design should be formally recorded.

at 800°C, the minimum oxygen concentration was as low as 4–7% v/v whereas at ambient temperatures, as determined in current practice, it is likely to be in the range 8–14% v/v. Temperature of the process is thus a consideration; on average there is a 1.4% fall in the minimum oxygen concentration for each 100°C temperature rise[8].

Note that reactions can occur between dusts and otherwise inert gases, eg metals and carbon dioxide. Such a possibility must be investigated and another inerting agent substituted.

The safety margin in practical applications depends on the efficiency of the oxygen monitoring system, the explosibility of the dust and size of plant. Typical values range from 1–4% below the limiting oxygen concentration, the lower values used only when monitoring is multi-point, and highly accurate, with dusts of low explosibility. If the dust is an St 3 dust, or there are likely to be extensive hot surfaces, the safety margin will be at the higher end of the range.

(27)   IS INERTING FEASIBLE?
If inerting is to be considered as a basis for safety it must be considered in relation to cost and operability. Factors to assess are:

- Inert gas costs;
- Typical inert gas leakage rates;
- Risks of asphyxiation;
- Monitoring system: reliability and compatibility.

2.2.1.5   LOGIC DIAGRAM FOR SUPPRESSION (FIGURE 2.6 — pages 40–41))
The pressure time characteristics and the maximum explosion pressure (P_{max}) are relevant to the application of suppression.

(28)   SUPPRESSION AS A BASIS OF SAFETY

(28.1)   APPLICABILITY OF A SUPPRESSION SYSTEM
Automatic explosion suppression systems are active systems comprised of explosion detector(s), high rate discharge explosion suppressor(s) and a central control unit. The detector(s) and suppressor(s) are mounted onto the plant component and are wired to the central control unit. Explosion suppression relies on the fact that there is a finite time between detection of the incipient explosion and the development of destructive pressure in the plant component. This time must be sufficient to allow effective deployment of a suppressant material — typically 20–40 ms. To determine the effectiveness of a suppression system it is necessary to know the explosion characteristics of the process material. As a general guide explosion suppression can normally be applied to most organic

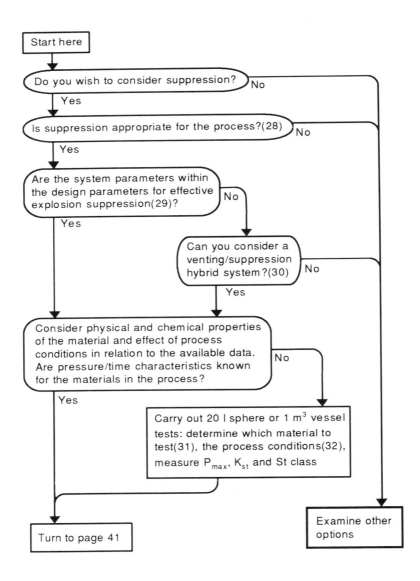

Figure 2.6   Logic diagram for suppression.
*   Formal definition of basis of safety — All practicable steps should be taken to avoid hazards. It is, therefore, strongly recommended that the basis of safety for the design should be formally recorded.

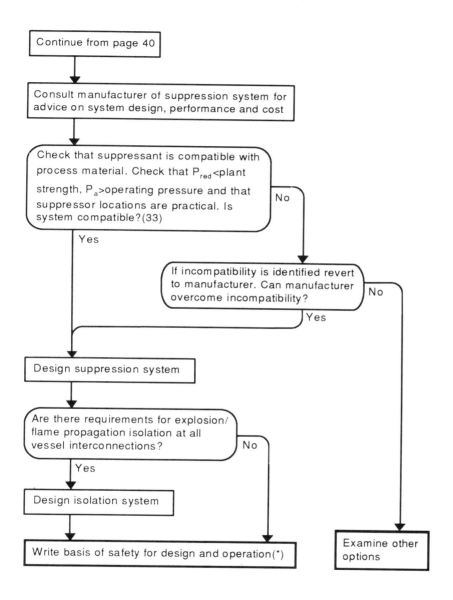

dusts, and to flammable vapour/dust mixtures, but not to metal dusts. Before deciding on this route for explosion safety the manufacturers of such systems should be consulted to confirm applicability.

(28.2)   COMPATIBILITY OF SUPPRESSANT WITH PROCESS MATERIALS

Suppressants deployed in suppression systems include liquids such as water and halogenated hydrocarbons and dry chemical powders based on either mono-ammonium phosphate or sodium bicarbonate. The compatibility of the suppressant with the process must be considered. It may be necessary to trade suppression effectiveness to a degree with suppressant compatibility — where for example a non-toxic suppressant or a vaporising suppressant is a process requirement. As a generalization dry chemical suppressants are more effective than most liquid suppressants against dust explosion incidents.

(28.3)   SHAPE AND SIZE OF EQUIPMENT

Since automatic explosion suppression systems operate by the injection of an extinguishing agent from a pressurised container into the process equipment there are upper and lower limits of vessel size that can be effectively protected because of limitations in suppressant deployment. For most materials the lower limit of process equipment volume is 0.25 m^3, and the upper limit of process equipment volume is 1000 m^3, and in pipelines with diameters up to 3 m. Larger volumes such as silos can be protected by suppression provided that their cylindrical diameter is less than 12 m.

(28.4)   PLANT PRESSURE SHOCK RESISTANCE

The maximum pressure attained in a suppressed dust explosion event depends on factors such as the explosion intensity (explosion characteristics of the process dust and the process turbulence), system activation pressure, type of suppressant and the number, type and deployment of high rate discharge explosion suppressors. In a typical system with an activation pressure set at 0.07 bar the suppressed explosion pressure transient would be 0.2–0.4 bar overpressure. Release of suppressant alone results in a pressure transient of about 0.05 bar. Equipment that is to be protected by suppression must be capable of withstanding the suppressed explosion overpressure transient.

(28.5)   EQUIPMENT LOCATION

Manufacturers will advise on equipment location. If these locations cannot be accommodated please refer back to the manufacturer since geometric location of the suppressors affects the projected worst case suppressed explosion pressure. Equipment must be located where it can be accessed for periodic checks and service.

(28.6)   OPERATING COSTS

Automatic explosion suppression systems, like all other explosion safety systems, must be maintained in good working order. Such installations require regular inspections by trained engineers, and the periodic change of 'lifed' components to maintain system reliability. The cost consequences of this maintenance should be considered at the system design stage. Maintenance will also require an occasional plant shut down — typically annually for up to 12 hours.

(29)   SUPPRESSION SYSTEM DESIGN PARAMETERS

(29.1)   APPLICABILITY

For most applications suppression systems are appropriate provided that dust is an St 1 or St 2 classed organic material. Some St 3 materials can be effectively protected but higher suppressed explosion pressures must be allowed for in the design.

(29.2)   REDUCED EXPLOSION PRESSURE, P_{red}

Manufacturers of explosion suppression systems will define the worst case reduced (suppressed) explosion pressure for an explosion event resulting from an ignition in the protected vessels based on the defined explosion intensity of the process dust. It is important to verify that the plant strength is sufficient to accommodate this pressure transient.

(29.3)   ACTIVATION PRESSURE, P_a

Most automatic explosion suppression systems are triggered by an accurately calibrated pressure sensor which is set to operate at a predetermined pressure threshold. It is essential to ensure that there is a significant margin between this activation pressure and both normal and abnormal process operating pressure if spurious release of suppressant is to be avoided. Some types of process plant may not be suitable for threshold pressure detection. In such circumstances detection by rate-of-rise in pressure or by flame detectors may be appropriate. Manufacturers should be consulted.

(29.4)   PREVENTION OF EMISSIONS

Explosion suppression is often selected as the safety means where the process materials are toxic, or could contaminate the environment if released. In such applications it is essential to remove any explosion relief vent from the protected plant component(s).

(29.5)   RELIABILITY

System reliability is both the assurance that the system will operate effectively in the event of an explosion incident, and the prevention of any spurious activation of the system.

Spurious activations of automatic explosion suppression systems are prevented by appropriate system design. However, it is unlikely that such events can be completely eliminated. Regular maintenance of such systems is essential both to minimize spurious activation and to maintain system reliability. Manufacturers' recommendations for maintenance and service must be adhered to. Most explosion suppression systems use explosive devices to operate the suppressors. In the UK it is necessary for the plant operator to obtain an explosives licence which is granted by the local police — even though handling of the explosive devices would normally be carried out only by the suppression system supplier. These explosive devices must be changed at set intervals to ensure system reliability.

As far as is known there are no instances where an automatic explosion suppression system has failed to avert an industrial explosion incident.

(30)   VENTING/SUPPRESSION HYBRID SYSTEM

A combination of explosion venting and explosion suppression can sometimes reduce the explosion pressure to the required value in circumstances where each technique used separately would be inadequate. Ignition of suppressant shortly after ignition will reduce the explosion violence and either generate lower reduced explosion pressures or allow the fitting of smaller vents. Injecting suppressant into the flame front near the vent opening will reduce the size of the fireball emitted from the vent[13]. Specialist help is required to design these systems.

(31)   WHICH TEST TO USE

The pressure-time characteristic of the material under test can be measured using the 20 litre sphere or 1 m³ bomb. Previously this was measured using the 1.2 litre Hartmann bomb, but this has been superseded, although data from it are available.

(32)   WHICH MATERIAL TO USE FOR THE PRESSURE TIME TEST

Often tests are done on samples as received. If the sample does not ignite it is sieved (75μ) and dried. This is the recommended test for the initial classification. If the user considers the drying conditions to be inappropriate to his process, the test will be repeated without drying. Materials classified as Group B at ambient temperature may be explosible when process temperatures are higher than ambient, or larger ignition sources are potentially present.

(33)   SYSTEM COMPATIBILITY

Check that the activation pressure of the suppressor is greater than the process operating pressure and the plant can withstand the reduced explosion pressure. Check that it is practicable to fit the required number and type of suppression to the plant.

(34)   EXPLOSION ISOLATION

Prevention of combustion wave propagation down interconnected pipelines must be considered for all containment, venting or suppression explosion protection systems. Explosion isolation can be by passive means such as rotary gate valves or explosion chokes, or by active means such as advanced inerting, triggered chemical barriers or slam shut valves.

Provided that appropriate explosion isolation measures are taken the design of explosion venting or explosion suppression systems can assume that ignition occurs within the confines of the protected vessel. Without appropriate explosion isolation the prospect of flame jet ignition down an interconnected pipeline into the vessel must be assumed and requirements for more rigorous explosion safety considered.

2.2.1.6   LOGIC DIAGRAM FOR VENTING (FIGURE 2.7 — pages 46–47))

The pressure time characteristic and the maximum explosion pressure (P_{max}) are relevant to the application of explosion venting.

The basic principle of venting is that if a dust explosion occurs in a vessel or container a vent of sufficient area should rapidly open and allow unburnt dust and explosion products to escape, thus limiting the pressure rise to an acceptable level.

For an explosion in a closed vessel the pressure rises in a manner illustrated in Figure 2.8 (curve A) on page 48. In the absence of a vent the pressure may rise to a maximum of 10 bar g or greater (P_{max}), which is a higher pressure than most plant can withstand. If a vent opens at a relatively low pressure the maximum pressure in the vessel will be limited as illustrated in Figure 2.8 (curve B). The so called 'reduced explosion pressure', P_{red}, will depend upon the size and location of the vent, the opening pressure (P_{stat}) and inertia of the vent cover, the presence of vent ducts, the state of the dust cloud and the presence of obstructions inside the vessel.

(35)   VENTING — GUIDELINES FOR ASSESSMENT

If venting is to be considered as a basis for safety it must be considered in relation to its suitability for the process; for example, a toxic emission through a vent may be unacceptable. Containment or suppression could be better for toxic materials where the danger from an emission could be serious.

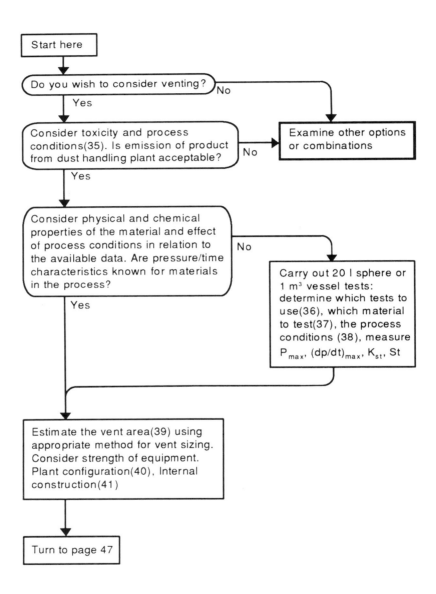

Figure 2.7   Logic diagram for venting.
* Formal definition of basis of safety — All practicable steps should be taken to avoid hazards. It is, therefore, strongly recommended that the basis of safety for the design should be formally recorded.

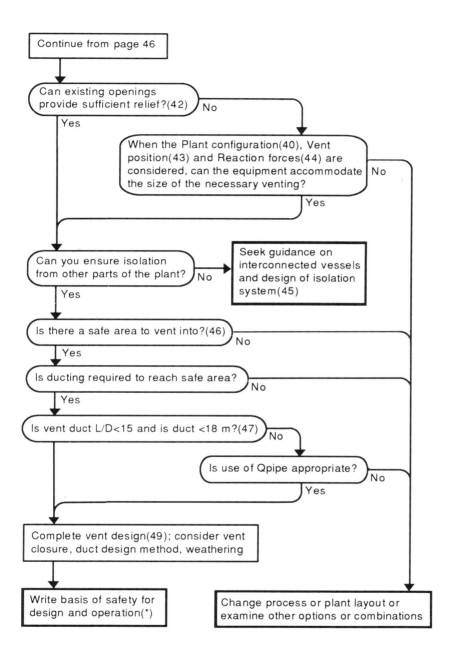

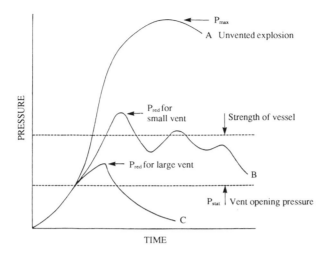

Figure 2.8   Typical pressure-time history of a vented and unvented explosion.
(Reproduced by permission of the Fire Research Station, BRE. Crown Copyright.)

There are circumstances where venting is an altogether inappropriate technique, either because it is unreliable, is not adequately researched or is itself dangerous.

Venting is inappropriate and should not be used when:

• The dust and/or its combustion products are excessively toxic or corrosive or both.

• The dust is violently explosible, ie outside the range over which vent estimation techniques can be applied.

• The dust is a detonating or deflagrating explosive (ie, will explode in the absence of atmospheric oxygen). Where detonations occur there is insufficient time for the vent to open to reduce the pressure.

• The vessel has a volume larger than 1000 m^3 (because the methods are not yet confirmed by experiment). Any method of protection is difficult at this scale of vessel.

In these circumstances, alternative precautions should be used and if necessary specialist advice sought.

A further consideration is that there may be circumstances where, although there are no objections to the venting technique, per se, it is nevertheless difficult to employ. There are often going to be borderline cases where, although venting may be an attractive option, its implementation is not easy. One example of this is a relatively small vessel such as a storage bin positioned inside a building but too far from an external wall for explosion products to be ducted to a safe place.

(36)   WHICH TEST TO USE

The pressure-time characteristic of the material under test can be measured using the 20 litre sphere or 1 m³ bomb. Previously this was measured using the 1.2 litre Hartmann bomb, but this has been superseded, although data from it are available. The modified Hartmann apparatus can be used to give a rapid assessment of dust explosion class for St 1 dusts.

(37)   WHICH MATERIAL TO USE FOR THE PRESSURE TIME TEST

Often tests are done on samples as received. If the sample does not ignite it should be tested under conditions of dryness and fineness appropriate to the process. Materials classified as Group B at ambient temperature may be explosible when process temperatures are higher than ambient, or larger ignition sources are potentially present.

(38)   RATE OF PRESSURE RISE — EFFECT OF PROCESS CONDITIONS

(38.1)   TEMPERATURE

The rate of pressure rise, dP/dt, may change significantly when the process temperature exceeds 50°C. Under these conditions dP/dt can be measured at the elevated temperature, if considered necessary.

(38.2)   PRESSURE

It is unusual to convey dusts at pressures greater than 2–3 bar g and below this the effect of pressure on the rate of pressure rise is minimal.

(38.3)   CONCENTRATION

Tests are normally carried out using a range of concentrations. The rate of pressure rise, dP/dt, increases with concentration and reaches a maximum in the 20 litre sphere at an optimum concentration somewhat higher than the stoichiometric concentration. At higher concentrations, dP/dt reduces, or stays roughly constant.

(38.4)   TURBULENCE

Dust clouds are usually turbulent to some degree because there must be some air movement if the dust is to remain dispersed. At low levels of turbulence the explosion violence of a dust cloud may be relatively mild, but at high states of turbulence, when the flame front is broken up and its effective area much increased, the explosion will propagate much more rapidly and the explosion violence will reach high values. This effect is very important in explosions moving through ducts and pipework because the confinement channels the air movement ahead of the explosion, generating high turbulence and driving the explosion to ever more rapid propagation. Constrictions and obstructions influence the development of turbulent explosions.

The level of turbulence can affect the venting requirements strongly; the greater the turbulence the faster the combustion rate, the faster the rate of pressure rise and thus the greater the area required to successfully vent the volume production caused by the explosion.

The rate of pressure rise is the important explosion parameter when determining the venting requirements of compact vessels. Standard methods for its determination and how it relates to the methods for estimating venting requirements are discussed in Chapter 3 and later chapters. The turbulent state of the dust cloud can, however, have a significant effect on the rate of pressure rise.

The standard 20 litre sphere or 1 m^3 tests, to be discussed fully in Chapter 3 and which form the basis for the nomograph methods for vent sizing (Chapter 4), are, for instance, done at a level of turbulence that simulates on the small scale that met with on the large scale in most industrial applications. It is well known that vent areas calculated using this data are generally satisfactory in all but the very worst cases.

When the turbulence level is less than that simulated in these standard tests then some reduction in vent area can, in principle, be made, although great care must be taken in the application of any methods which rely on a presumed lower turbulence. A thorough knowledge of the details of both the industrial process and the limitations of the vent sizing method are crucial.

Assessing turbulence levels in industrial plant is difficult and there are many problems associated with the application of any such measurements. Under normal working turbulence levels may be relatively low, but an explosion elsewhere in the plant or an incipient explosion in the particular item of equipment may generate turbulence levels (possibly due to internal obstructions, flow through pipes and ducts, etc) that are well above those met normally. These complications can be important for venting in real life situations.

The rate of pressure rise, dP/dt, can vary by a factor of ten when changing from static to turbulent conditions. Turbulence can only be studied in detail if full scale test facilities are available.

A secondary influence on the rate of pressure rise and the consequent venting requirements is the strength of the ignition source. The most used standard test uses a strong, localized, ignition source made up of two 5 kJ chemical igniters (Chapter 3). In practice many likely ignition sources will have much lower energies. There may, however, be circumstances, for example a flame entering a vessel as a jet from a conduit connection, where the ignition source can be very large, can result in a very rapid rate of combustion and can have an important effect on the venting requirements.

These particulars need to be considered before a decision to employ explosion venting is made, and when the venting requirements are being estimated. As much information as possible about the process, likely ignition sources and state of the dust cloud inside the plant must be collected if an effective calculation of vent area is to be made.

(38.5)   MOISTURE CONTENT
See comment under (7).

(38.6)   SCALE OF THE VESSEL AND SIZE OF DUST CLOUD
The violence of a dust explosion — as indicated by the rate of pressure rise — depends on the size of the vessel. The larger the vessel the slower the rate of pressure rise, although the potential for destruction will be greater because of the increased scale of the explosion. One of the simplest scaling laws is the cubic law which relates the rate of pressure rise in an explosion to the cube root of the vessel volume, and is used to calculate the K_{st} value from measurements of $(dP/dt)_{max}$ in the 20 litre sphere apparatus.

The size of vents required to limit the pressure rise to a prescribed level depends upon the volume of the vessel.

In the simplest situation it is assumed that the dust cloud is uniformly distributed throughout the vessel, ie the volume of the explosible dust cloud is equal to the volume of the vessel. Indeed, in some of the test equipment to be described in Chapter 3 the procedure is designed to ensure that this is the case. In practice the volume of the explosible dust cloud may be significantly less than the volume of the vessel. If so, the pressure rise will be less than for the case of uniform dust dispersion, provided the ignition is not in such a position that the dust cloud expands to fill the vessel before the flame arrives at the vent. However, work has shown that reduced pressures in vessels where the dust cloud only partially filled the vessel were similar to those where the dust cloud totally filled the vessel[8].

Where the provision of sufficient vent area (based on the vessel volume) may be practically difficult or expensive and where there may be good reason for suspecting that the explosible dust cloud may be smaller than the vessel volume, the possibility of basing the vent design on the supposed dust cloud volume rather than the vessel volume appears attractive. However, it is recommended that in methods for assessing venting requirements the actual volume of the vessel should be used rather than the dust cloud volume, unless specialist knowledge indicates otherwise. In some applications such as in certain types of spray drier the volume of an explosible dust cloud, in normal operation, will be significantly smaller than the volume of the vessel. However, there may also be quantities of dust deposited on either the walls of the vessel or other internal structures, or held in the base. In the event of an explosion the initial size of the dust cloud could be rapidly increased because of the entrainment of deposited dust stirred up due to the effects of the initial explosion. Unless a great deal is known about the processes involved there can be little certainty in determining the size of dust clouds smaller than the containing vessels. The whole volume should be used in assessing venting requirements.

(39)   VENT AREA CALCULATION
This is the subject of Chapter 4 onwards.

(40)   PLANT CONFIGURATION
Test work is carried out in equipment having dimensions in the ratio 1:1:1 ($L/D = 1$). Although most process vessels have $L/D < 3$, and therefore reasonably close to $L/D = 1$, plant configuration is the area in which there is most need for experimental data. Work has shown that pressure effects can be markedly enhanced as L/D increases.

(41)   INTERNAL CONSTRUCTION
In some applications, usually involving relatively small vessels, it may be impractical to provide the vessel with explosion vents and the vessel must be designed to withstand the maximum explosion pressure, P_{max}, without rupture. In some small enclosures the maximum explosion pressure is reduced below that measured in standard tests because of cooling caused by large internal areas provided by components, eg mills.

When a vessel is not designed to pressure vessel codes, the difficulty of estimating its strengths should not be underestimated. It is the strength of the weakest part of the vessel that must be known, be it weld, join, junction, etc and this determines the explosion pressure which the vessel can withstand. Quantifying the strength of weak plant, especially when it is old and has been in service for some time, is not easy.

(42)   CAN EXISTING OPENINGS PROVIDE SUFFICIENT RELIEF?
In small compact vessels the process entry and exit ports may provide a satisfactory amount of venting, although due consideration must be paid to

preventing a propagation of an explosion into other items of plant and other parts of the process. With full information as to how the maximum explosion pressure is limited by internal components and on the enclosure's inherent venting it may be that small vessels especially can be designed so that no extra venting is required. A convincing case would need to be made, and the justification for this option would need to be well documented.

(43)   VENT POSITION
The flame front must have free and unimpeded access to the vent.

(44)   REACTION FORCES
The ejection of the explosion from a vent may produce reaction forces which may damage a vessel if the forces are too unbalanced.

(45)   EXPLOSION ISOLATION
Prevention of combustion wave propagation down interconnected pipelines must be considered for all containment, venting or suppression explosion protection systems. Explosion isolation can be by passive means such as rotary gate valves or explosion chokes, or by active means such as advanced inerting, triggered chemical barriers or slam shut valves.

Provided that appropriate explosion isolation measures are taken the design of explosion venting or explosion suppression systems can assume that ignition occurs within the confines of the protected vessel. Without appropriate explosion isolation the prospect of flame jet ignition down an interconnected pipeline into the vessel must be assumed and requirements for more rigorous explosion safety considered.

There is one other consideration in the practical application of venting. It is usually good practice to provide interlocks so that, in the event of an explosion and the bursting of a vent closure, all or parts of the process are automatically shut down.

It is for instance vital for dust conveying to be stopped because smouldering or burning clumps of dust remaining after the explosion can be transferred into adjacent items of plant where they can act as ignition sources for further explosions. Screw conveyors and rotary locks are obvious examples of conveying equipment that should be stopped as rapidly as is possible.

(46)   SAFE DISCHARGE AREA
The vent must be sited to prevent injuries to personnel and to minimize the effects of fire and blast. Deflector plates are normally used. Hazard analysis may provide guidance to define a safe area. Exclusion of personnel from the discharge area is a relevant consideration.

Figure 2.9   Vented dust explosion. (Courtesy DCE Ltd.)

The volume of flame ejected by a vented explosion can be large and although it is best practice to site vented plant in the open air, where this is impracticable the burning cloud should be ducted to a safe place outside the building. Flame, unburnt dust that can then inflame outside the vent and explosion overpressures are all ejected from the vent opening. Personnel must be excluded from the discharge areas of vents or vent ducts during normal operation. Deflectors can be installed to guide the vented explosion to a safe place.

Explosion venting inside buildings is viable only when the vent discharges into an enclosed area from which personnel are completely excluded when the plant is operating. As well as procedures for excluding personnel from the vicinity of the vent, the strength of the building, its internal design and the dangers of secondary explosions must all be considered if venting into an enclosed area has to take place. Under no circumstances must secondary explosions be allowed to develop. The blast from the vented explosion will disturb dust layers and other accumulations that have collected in the work-place, dispersing them into the air and producing a cloud which will fuel an explosion of much more destructive potential than the original event. These secondary explosions can be extensive and good housekeeping must ensure that dust accumulations are not allowed to build up in any location. Explosible clouds can form from very thin layers of dust.

(47)   DUCTING DESIGN METHOD
Design methods for vent ducting are available (see Chapter 7).

(48)   Q-PIPE
A Q-pipe is a device for quenching the flame when it ejects from an explosion vent. It is essentially a large flame arrester. Although experimentation has shown it to be a promising device in principle, its use should be validated in the full scale for a particular situation.

(49)   COMPLETE THE VENT DESIGN
Sufficient work has been published on vent closure design to allow this to be done.

The proper design of an explosion vent will result in the safe discharge of the explosion without otherwise splitting the vessel walls. Figure 2.9 shows a successfully vented dust explosion.

3. DETERMINATION OF DUST EXPLOSION CHARACTERISTICS

In this chapter the standard tests for assessing the explosibility of a dust and quantifying this explosibility are described.

3.1 EXPLOSIBILITY CLASSIFICATION

The first stage in the design of explosion prevention and protection systems is to obtain a qualitative assessment of the ability of a dust to take part in an explosion. These are explosibility tests and in the UK are used to divide dusts into two groups:

Group A — dusts which are able to ignite and propagate a flame;
Group B — dusts which do not propagate a flame.

It is important that this classification pertains to the conditions under which the dust will be handled. It is not sensible, for instance, to conduct an explosibility assessment at room temperature when the process temperature is to be several hundred degrees. Dusts which can be classified as Group B at room temperature can readily be shown to ignite if the temperature is higher. A series of tests has thus been devised which allows explosion classification under increasingly severe conditions.

3.1.1 THE STANDARD EXPLOSIBILITY TESTS

As in all explosion testing the sample selected for testing must be representative of the material in the plant at risk. It may be that a random sample of the dust or powder will result in a Group A classification, but it is best practice to ensure that the sample is as dry as the driest material in the plant and that the size distribution of the test dust is similar to the finest size fractions that are likely to occur in any part of the process. If in doubt the driest sample of dust less than 75 µm should be selected.

The standard explosibility test currently accepted by the Health and Safety Executive is the vertical tube test, which is described in detail by Field[1].

The vertical tube apparatus is shown in Figure 3.1. The usual ignition source is an electric spark produced by a high voltage transformer having a 10 kV, 0.024 amp output, and bridging a 0.5 cm gap between electrodes. Some dusts do not ignite readily by electric spark and an alternative ignition source is a heated wire coil made from 20 SWG Kanthal 'A' wire and consisting of about

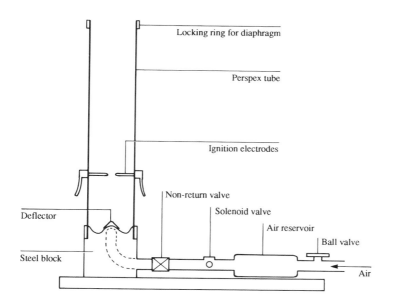

Locking ring for diaphragm

Perspex tube

Ignition electrodes

Non-return valve

Deflector

Solenoid valve

Air reservoir

Ball valve

Steel block

Air

Figure 3.1   Vertical tube apparatus, coil ignition. (Reproduced by permission of the Fire Research Station, BRE. Crown Copyright.)

eight turns with an external diameter of 1 cm. The coil is heated to approximately 1000°C by a transformer having an output of 10 volts and 20 amps.

The dust is dispersed vertically from the dispersion cup around the mushroom-shaped deflector by either an instantaneous or continuous blast of air. If flame propagation is observed in the tube the dust is designated Group A. If flame propagation is not observed then the amount of dust and the method of dispersion is varied. If flame propagation is still not observed further drying and sieving of the sample takes place. The dried and sieved fractions are tested individually so that a Group B classification is based on exhaustive testing.

It should be borne in mind that this classification is only valid in air at ambient conditions of temperature and pressure. In dust-handling processes such as drying, where high temperatures exist, the Group B classification may no longer be relevant. It is quite possible for a dust classified as Group B at room temperatures to have a dust cloud minimum ignition temperature.

3.1.2 TESTS AT ELEVATED TEMPERATURES

The Godbert-Greenwald furnace apparatus (see Figure 3.2) is used to assess dust explosibility at elevated temperatures. It is generally proposed[1] that if a dust with a Group B classification is to be used at temperatures above 110°C, then further testing is necessary. Group A dusts need no further testing.

The Godbert-Greenwald furnace is described by Field[1]. It comprises a 21.6 cm long, 3.6 cm i.d. vitreosil tube wound with 20 SWG Kanthal 'A' wire which gives an even temperature distribution along the length of the tube. The tube is mounted vertically in a 20 SWG stainless steel, 15 cm diameter cylinder, and furnace temperatures up to 1000°C can be obtained. Explosibility testing is done at 800°C.

A small amount of the Group B dust, typically 0.2 g, is placed in the dust holder. The dust is dispersed into the furnace tube by an air blast. The criterion for ignition is that flames are observed at the bottom of the tube. If no flame propagation occurs the dust is thoroughly tested by varying the dust amount and the dispersion conditions. If flame propagation occurs during the sequence of tests, the dust is re-classified as Group A; if no flame is observed the dust remains in the Group B classification.

This result can be accepted as the final assessment but, because the test is a severe one, further testing can be done if process conditions are known to be less severe[1]. The furnace test can be performed at the known temperature of the process and with a localized ignition source inside the furnace tube. If flame propagation is observed the dust is classified as Group A.

Dusts which remain classified as Group B may require further testing in either the 20 litre sphere or 1 m³ vessel.

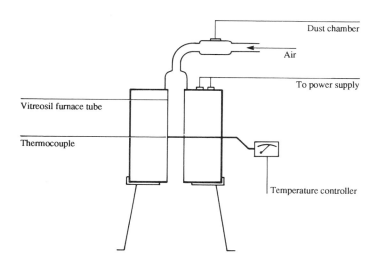

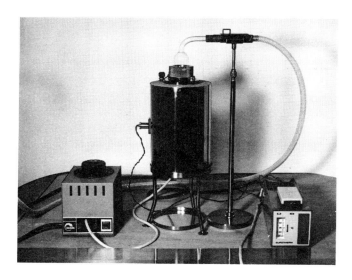

Figure 3.2   Godbert-Greenwald furnace. (Reproduced by permission of the Fire Research Station, BRE. Crown Copyright.)

3.1.3   FURTHER EXPLOSIBILITY TESTS

Further explosibility testing can be done in either the 20 litre sphere (with a central 2 kJ ignition source) or 1 m^3 vessel (with a central 10 kJ ignition source). The explosibility is then judged on the basis of the pressure rise. If a pressure rise of less than 0.5 bar is recorded for all dust concentrations across the explosible range the dust is considered to be non-explosible, ie Group B. Otherwise the dust is allocated to Group A as an explosible dust.

3.2   EXPLOSION CHARACTERISTICS

The tests for explosibility described in Section 3.1 give only a qualitative assessment of the risk. A quantitative assessment requires further testing to measure explosion characteristics which are important to the design of explosion protection methods.

These explosion characteristics are:

• The maximum explosion pressure, P_{max}. This is the highest explosion pressure developed by an enclosed dust explosion. It is measured in a standard test at the optimum dust concentration.

• The maximum rate of pressure rise, $(dP/dt)_{max}$. This is the highest rate of pressure rise generated by an enclosed dust explosion. It is measured in a standard test at the optimum dust concentration.

3.2.1   TEST METHODS

1 M^3 VESSEL

The 1 m^3 vessel is described in detail by Bartknecht[7]. It is recognised as an accepted international standard test apparatus and is shown in Figure 3.3. The explosion vessel is pressure-resistant and has a length approximately equal to its diameter. The dust is introduced into a 5.4 litre dust container external to the main vessel but connected to it through a fast-acting valve. The dust is held under an air pressure of 20 bar and is dispersed into the 1 m^3 vessel through a semi-annular, perforated half-ring with 13 holes each of 6 mm diameter. This procedure is often called the VDI method of dust injection. It is often used by researchers to inject dust into larger vessels, for instance silos[28], so that correspondence between the state of the dust clouds on the large and small scale can be made. After an ignition delay, t_d, of 0.6 s, the dust cloud is ignited by an ignition source positioned at the centre of the vessel. The ignition source comprises two pyrotechnical igniters, and has a total energy of 10 kJ.

The development of the explosion pressure with time is monitored, and the peak values of maximum explosion pressure and maximum rate of pressure obtained after testing over a wide range of dust concentrations. If, at large dust

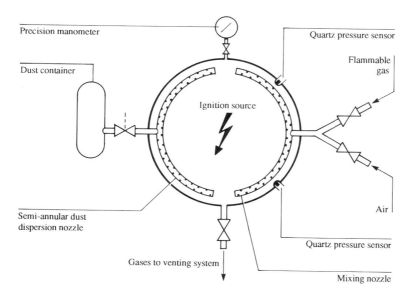

Figure 3.3   Test apparatus ($V = 1\,m^3$) for the determination of explosion data of combustible dusts (schematic) (Reproduced from Bartnecht, W., 1989, *Explosions. Course, prevention, protection* (Springer-Verlag) by permission of the author and publisher.)

concentrations a 5.4 litre dust container proves too small to contain the dust, a 10 litre container can be used. However, the value of t_d must be changed to 0.9 s so that results when using the 10 litre container are comparable to those with a 5.4 litre container.

20 LITRE SPHERICAL TESTER

The 20 litre spherical dust tester is a smaller version of the 1 m³ test vessel described above, and is shown in Figure 3.4 on page 62. It is fully described by Bartknecht[7]. Prior to testing the dust is confined in a 600 ml dust container external to the 20 litre sphere but connected to it through a fast acting valve. The dust is held under an air pressure of 20 bar and is dispersed into the sphere through a perforated half-ring system with 112 holes each of 3 mm diameter. The ignition delay, t_d, is 0.06 s (60 ms). Before a test the 20 litre sphere is evacuated to a pressure of 0.4 bar absolute. When the dust is injected the pressure rises to 1 bar absolute and the explosion is thus ignited at normal atmospheric pressure. The ignition source comprises pyrotechnical igniters with a total energy of 10 kJ positioned at the vessel centre. The peak values of maximum explosion pressure and maximum rate of pressure rise are obtained after testing over a range of dust concentrations.

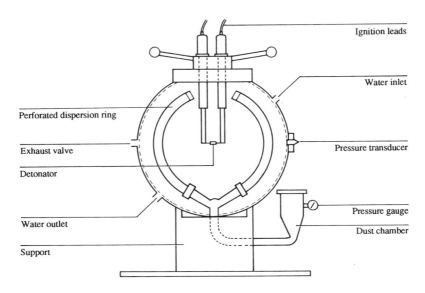

Ignition leads

Water inlet

Perforated dispersion ring

Exhaust valve

Pressure transducer

Detonator

Water outlet

Pressure gauge

Dust chamber

Support

Figure 3.4   20 litre spherical explosion apparatus. (Reproduced by permission of the Fire Research Station, BRE. Crown Copyright.)

TABLE 3.1

Definition of dust explosion classes (1 m^3 apparatus, 10 kJ ignition source)

Dust explosion class	K_{st} (bar m s^{-1})	Characteristics
St 0	0	Non-explosible
St 1	$0 < K_{st} < 200$	Weak to moderately explosible
St 2	$200 < K_{st} < 300$	Strongly explosible
St 3	$300 < K_{st}$	Very strongly explosible

The peak value of the maximum rate of pressure rise $(dP/dt)_{max}$, is used to calculate a dust specific explosibility characteristic called the K_{st} value. (K_{st} is the VDI designation; the ISO designation for the same quantity is K_{max}.) The K_{st} value is given by:

$$K_{st} = (dP/dt)_{max} V^{1/3} \tag{1}$$

where $(dP/dt)_{max}$ is the peak maximum rate of pressure rise (bar/s) and V is the total volume of the vessel (m^3). The units of K_{st} are bar m/s. The K_{st} value is derived only from measurements in either the 1 m^3 vessel or the 20 litre sphere.

Comparisons of results from the 1 m^3 vessel and the 20 litre spherical tester generally show that[8]:

• The values for the maximum explosion pressure, P_{max}, measured in the 20 litre sphere are slightly lower than those measured in the 1 m^3 apparatus;

• The K_{st} values are equal up to about 600 bar m s^{-1}.

The K_{st} value can be used to classify dusts into one of several groups. Table 3.1 shows the classification that is generally adopted.

Equation (1) is known as the 'cubic law' or 'cube root law'. K_{st} is considered to be a constant for any dust, independent of vessel size, and equation (1) acts as a simple scaling law. However, there are limitations to the conditions under which this scaling law is strictly applicable. In practical terms this means that if any other apparatus is used, it must be calibrated against the 1 m^3 or 20 litre standard test vessels.

Any deviation from the established procedure requires an alteration in the ignition delay, t_d, until concurrence with measurements in the 1 m^3 vessel is obtained.

The 20 litre spherical tester is recommended as a standard explosibility test in many countries including the USA and the UK. Some particles with long

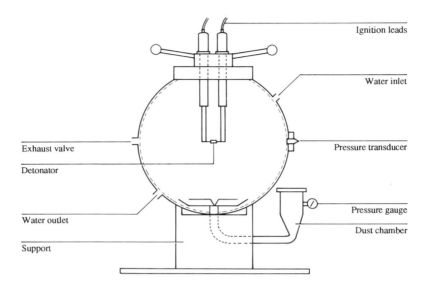

Figure 3.5   Modified 20 litre spherical explosion apparatus. (Reproduced by permission of the Fire Research Station, BRE. Crown Copyright.)

L/D ratios may prove difficult to disperse. To overcome this problem a modified 20 litre sphere apparatus has been introduced.

A diagram of the modified 20 litre spherical test vessel is shown in Figure 3.5. It is to all intents and purposes identical to the original 20 litre test vessel apart from the method of dust dispersion. Instead of the annular ring system there is a deflector plate near to the point of dust injection. Comparative tests with a number of powders have indicated that with the recommended test procedures the measurements from the original and modified vessels are comparable.

THE HARTMANN APPARATUS

Dust explosion characteristics have been measured for many years in the Hartmann apparatus developed by the US Bureau of Mines. A full description is given by Field[1], and the device is shown in Figure 3.6.

The Hartmann vessel is a totally enclosed and stronger version of the vertical tube apparatus. It comprises a cylinder with a volume of 1.2 litres and has provision for either electric spark ignition or a hot coil. A pressure transducer is incorporated in the lid. A small amount of dust, about 0.1 g initially, is placed in the dispersion cup and then blown into a suspension around the ignition source by release of 50 cm^3 of air pressurized to 8.3 bar. The pressure-time development

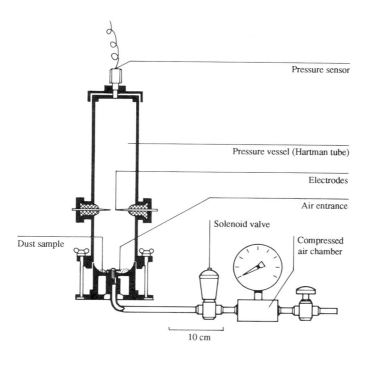

Pressure sensor

Pressure vessel (Hartman tube)

Electrodes

Air entrance

Solenoid valve

Compressed air chamber

Dust sample

10 cm

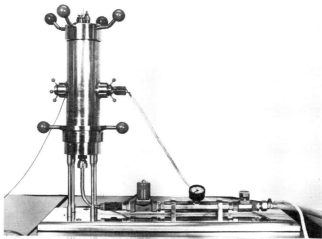

Figure 3.6 Hartmann bomb. (Diagram reproduced from Bartnecht, W., 1989, *Explosions. Course, prevention, protection* (Springer-Verlag) by permission of the author and publisher, photograph reproduced by permission of the Fire Research Station, BRE. Crown Copyright.)

65

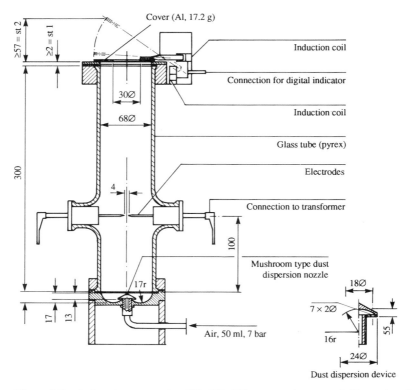

Figure 3.7   Laboratory apparatus, 'Modified Hartmann-Apparatus'. (Reproduced from Bartnecht, W., 1989, *Explosions. Course, prevention, protection* (Springer-Verlag) by permission of the author and publisher.)

of the explosion is measured; the dust concentration is assumed equal to the amount of dust introduced into the cylinder divided by the cylinder volume.

The Hartmann apparatus has been criticized for its small volume. The wall of the cylinder is close to the ignition point and the flame soon impinges on it with a corresponding cooling effect. There are also difficulties in specifying accurately the concentration of dust which undergoes ignition. The Hartmann apparatus has been superseded by the 1 m³ vessel and 20 litre spherical tester, although the data from it still has some part to play in application of techniques for the assessment of vent areas.

The peak explosion pressure and peak maximum rate of pressure rise measured in the Hartmann apparatus cannot be used to calculate a K_{st} value for a dust; the dust explosion conditions are too dissimilar compared to the 20 litre sphere or 1 m³ vessel. Because of the wall effect, P_{max} and $(dP/dt)_{max}$ are less than would be measured in a spherical vessel. Scaling to larger volumes is difficult. Explosibility characteristics from the Hartmann apparatus cannot be used with vent-estimating techniques designed for use with the K_{st} value. Likewise, explosion characteristics measured in the 20 litre sphere or 1 m³ vessel must not be used with vent-estimating techniques designed for use with data from the Hartmann apparatus.

One modification of the Hartmann apparatus has been used as a means of gauging the likely explosion hazard without giving quantitative data. Instead of being totally enclosed, the Hartmann tube is fitted at the top with a hinged lid (Figure 3.7). The dust is dried under vacuum at a temperature of 40–50°C, perhaps after milling to a particle size less than 30 μm. The dust sample is placed in the dispersion cup and lifted into suspension around the ignition source by air from a reservoir pressurized to 7 bar. The dust class is indicated by the angle of the hinged cover after the explosion, although if the flame extends at least half the length of the tube without lifting the cover the dust is considered to be St 1. Bartknecht[7] suggests that dusts classified as St 1 dusts in the modified Hartmann apparatus can be considered to be St 1 dusts, but that dusts classified as St 2 by displacement of the cover cannot be differentiated between St 1, St 2 or St 3 dusts. This is only a qualitative test which is useful as a screening device for explosible dusts. Further testing is necessary if quantitative data is required.

3.3   WHERE TO GO FOR TESTS

The following laboratories in the UK are able to carry out the above tests on a commercial basis:

Building Research Establishment
Fire Research Station
Borehamwood
Hertfordshire
WD6 2BL

Imperial Chemical Industries
PO Box 42
Hexagon House
Blackley
Manchester
M9 3DA

Chilworth Technology Limited
Beta House
Chilworth Research Centre
Southampton
SO1 7NS

4. SIZING OF VENTS — THE BASIC METHODS

Safe sizing of vent openings is the most important design parameter in the application of explosion venting.

Many methods for sizing vents have been proposed. However, they are not all applicable in all circumstances. Any attempt to apply a single method indiscriminately may lead either to uneconomic and impractically large vents or, more seriously, to inadequate vents which could result in extensive damage and injury.

The process of choosing the most effective method of vent sizing can be complex and, if carried to an extreme, requires a great deal of information about both the plant and the process.

The basic and most commonly used vent sizing techniques for compact vessels require only the minimum of information. The results derived from these techniques have been shown to be reliable in practice, and it is recommended that these methods are used unless there is an overwhelming reason for using one of the less common methods. The basic methods may prove conservative in some applications, and a move away from the basic methods can be occasioned by economic or practical considerations. It may, for instance, prove difficult to fit large vents on some plant whereas details of the process provide an effective argument for fitting smaller vents. If the predictions are to be refined, the amount of information required increases; especially that pertaining to the state of the dust cloud itself.

The logic diagram in Figure 4.1 is an attempt to chart a path through the questions that need to be asked, the decisions that have to be taken and the provisos that have to be considered before a final choice of vent sizing technique can be safely made. Obviously, the more basic the method the less time and trouble this journey will take.

The basic vent sizing techniques most commonly used for compact modern plant — often based on a considerable amount of experimental evidence and industrial experience — are described in this chapter. The consideration of complicating factors which may require modifications to these methods — or the application of different methods altogether — is left to later chapters.

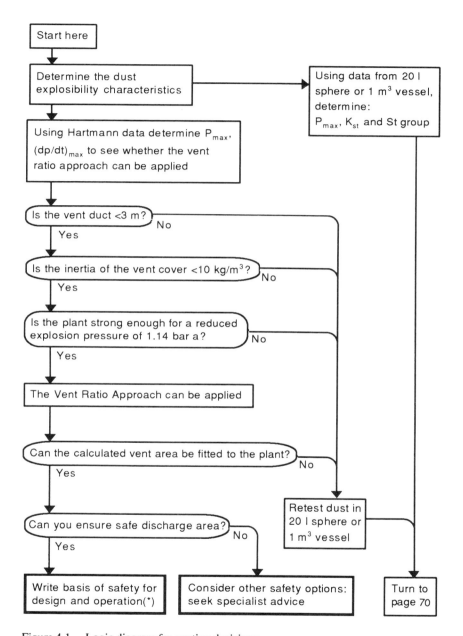

Figure 4.1   Logic diagram for venting decisions.
*   Formal definition of basis of safety — All practicable steps should be taken to avoid hazards. It is, therefore, strongly recommended that the basis of safety for the design should be formally recorded.

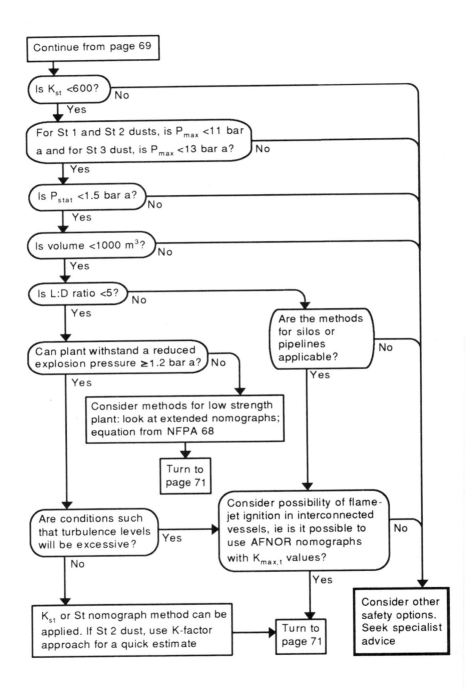

Continue from page 69

Is K_{st} <600? — No

Yes

For St 1 and St 2 dusts, is P_{max} <11 bar a and for St 3 dust, is P_{max} <13 bar a? — No

Yes

Is P_{stat} <1.5 bar a? — No

Yes

Is volume <1000 m³? — No

Yes

Is L:D ratio <5? — No

Yes

Are the methods for silos or pipelines applicable? — No

Yes

Can plant withstand a reduced explosion pressure ≥1.2 bar a? — No

Yes

Consider methods for low strength plant: look at extended nomographs; equation from NFPA 68

Turn to page 71

Consider possibility of flame-jet ignition in interconnected vessels, ie is it possible to use AFNOR nomographs with $K_{max,t}$ values? — No

Are conditions such that turbulence levels will be excessive? — Yes

No

Yes

K_{st} or St nomograph method can be applied. If St 2 dust, use K-factor approach for a quick estimate

Turn to page 71

Consider other safety options. Seek specialist advice

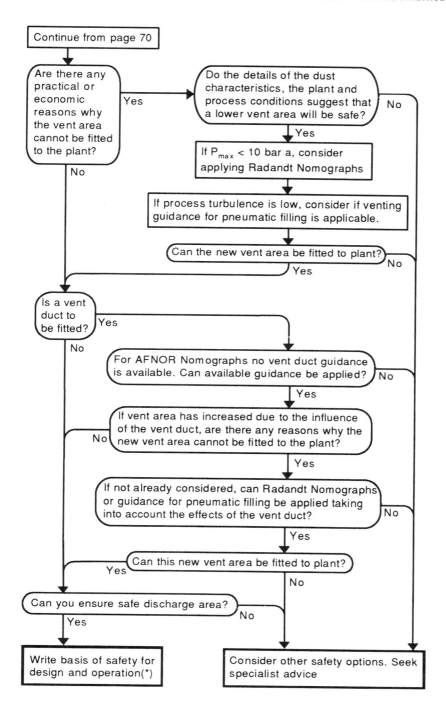

Continue from page 70

Are there any practical or economic reasons why the vent area cannot be fitted to the plant?

Yes

No

Do the details of the dust characteristics, the plant and process conditions suggest that a lower vent area will be safe?

No

Yes

If P_{max} < 10 bar a, consider applying Radandt Nomographs

If process turbulence is low, consider if venting guidance for pneumatic filling is applicable.

Can the new vent area be fitted to plant?

No

Yes

Is a vent duct to be fitted?

Yes

No

For AFNOR Nomographs no vent duct guidance is available. Can available guidance be applied?

No

Yes

If vent area has increased due to the influence of the vent duct, are there any reasons why the new vent area cannot be fitted to the plant?

No

Yes

If not already considered, can Radandt Nomographs or guidance for pneumatic filling be applied taking into account the effects of the vent duct?

No

Yes

Can this new vent area be fitted to plant?

Yes

No

Can you ensure safe discharge area?

No

Yes

Write basis of safety for design and operation(*)

Consider other safety options. Seek specialist advice

71

Essentially, four quantities need to be known before a proper estimation of the vent area can be made. These are:

- The reduced explosion pressure. This is the explosion pressure that should not be exceeded and which depends on the strength of the vessel. This is generally designated P_{red} and has units of bar. P_{red} should not exceed two thirds of the burst pressure. It may be that the strength of the vessel is not accurately known, and such a lack of information must be an important consideration when deciding which method of vent area calculation to use.

- The vessel volume. Most of the basic methods for estimating vent areas are limited to compact enclosures with length to diameter (L/D) ratios less than 5. Methods for sizing vents in silos and pipelines are available and are discussed in Chapter 6.

- The explosibility of the dust. The explosibility data must be appropriate to the vent sizing method being used.

- The characteristics of the vent cover. The bursting pressure of the vent cover is an important parameter when calculating the vent area. The inertia of the vent cover will also influence the size of vent necessary.

This chapter concludes with some worked examples which demonstrate the different methods and show comparisons between them.

4.1   THE VDI NOMOGRAPH METHODS

4.1.1   THE K_{st} NOMOGRAPH METHOD

The K_{st} nomograph method for assessment of vent area was devised from the theoretical work of Heinrich[29] and the experimental work of Bartknecht[7] and Donat[30]. The method has found widespread use throughout Europe[17,18], the United States[16] and elsewhere. It is generally considered to be the best method and the recommendation is that when the situation and the information available permit, this is the method to use.

The information required for the K_{st} nomograph is:

- The reduced explosion pressure (bar a);

- The volume of the dust-handling plant (m^3);

- The explosibility characteristic — the K_{st} value of the dust as measured in a standard test (bar m s^{-1});

- The static opening pressure of the vent cover, P_{stat} (bar a). It is assumed that the vent has low inertia with an area density less than 10 kg/m^2. No provision is made for vent covers of high inertia.

The theoretical model developed by Heinrich[29], utilizing experimental data from Donat[30], has been used to design a series of nomographs which are reproduced in Figures 4.2, and 4.3 and 4.4 (see pages 74–79). Each of the nomographs is applicable for a given value of the vent bursting pressure, P_{stat}. The method of using the nomographs is shown on Figure 4.2. A worked example is given at the end of this chapter.

The published nomographs are applicable in the following conditions:

- Vent bursting pressures, P_{stat}, greater than 1.1 bar a;
- Reduced explosion pressures, P_{red}, greater than 1.2 bar a;
- K_{st} values greater than 10 bar m s^{-1} and less than 600 bar m s^{-1};
- Values of P_{max} less than 11 bar a for St 1 and St 2 dusts and P_{max} values less than 13 bar a for St 3 dusts;
- Vessel volumes less than 1000 m^3;
- Length to diameter ratio of the vessel less than 5:1;
- No vent ducts are fitted to the vent.

The original published nomographs[17] were limited to K_{st} values between 50 bar m s^{-1} and 600 bar m s^{-1}, but they have been extended to lower values[14], and it is the extended version that is given here.

4.1.2   THE ST GROUP NOMOGRAPH METHOD

A similar series of nomographs has been published which ranks dusts in the three St groups — St 1, St 2 and St 3 (see Section 3.2.1 on page 60). These nomographs are reproduced in Figures 4.5, and 4.6 and 4.7 (see pages 80–85), and the method of their use is shown in Figure 4.5. A worked example is given at the end of this chapter.

The St nomographs are based on the experimental data rather than Heinrich's theory, so differences do exist between these nomographs and the K_{st} nomographs. For instance, the St 1 line in the St nomographs will not exactly coincide with the $K_{st} = 200$ bar m s^{-1} from the K_{st} nomographs. The differences are slight, however, although obviously if the dust has a low K_{st} value within its specific St group, the St nomographs are bound to over-size the vent area, a result which may be of practical or economic importance.

4.1.3   REGRESSION ANALYSES FROM THE K_{st} NOMOGRAPHS

In recent years, equations have been fitted to the original K_{st} nomographs published in VDI 3673. These are not theoretical derivations, but are regression analyses, and the equations can be used for rapid calculation of vent area using computer programs.

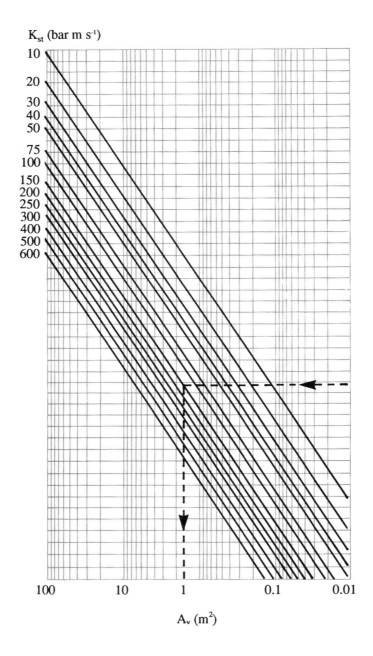

Figure 4.2   Extended nomograph: $P_{stat} = 1.1$ bar a.

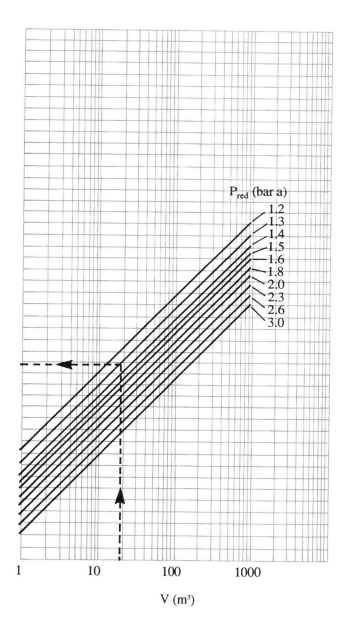

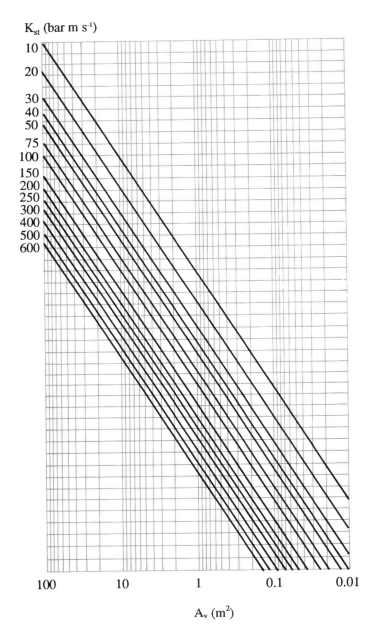

Figure 4.3   Extended nomograph: P_{stat} = 1.2 bar a.

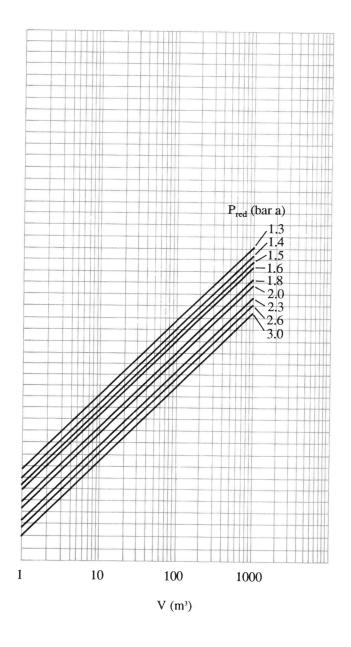

K_{st} (bar m s^{-1})

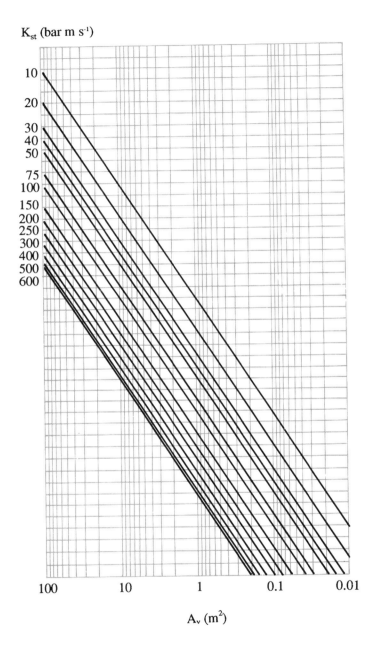

A_v (m^2)

Figure 4.4   Extended nomograph: P_{stat} = 1.5 bar a.

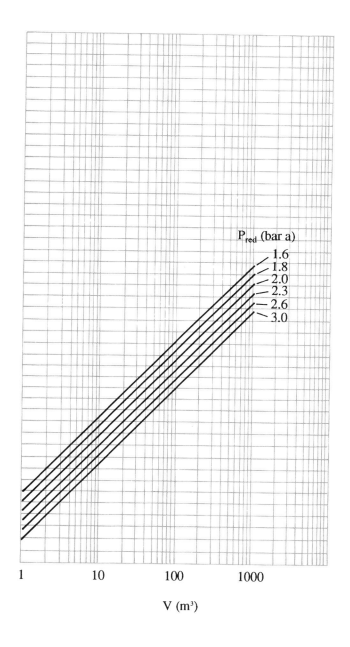

P_{red} (bar a)

1.6
1.8
2.0
2.3
2.6
3.0

1   10   100   1000

V (m³)

An equation developed by Simpson[31] is recommended in NFPA 68[16]:

$$A/V^{2/3} = a\,K_{st}^b\,P_{red}^c \tag{4}$$

where a = 0.000571 exp $[2P_{stat}]$

b = 0.978 exp $[-0.105P_{stat}]$

c = -0.687 exp $[0.226P_{stat}]$

where P_{stat} and P_{red} are bar g, K_{st} is bar m s^{-1}, V is m^3 and A_v is m^2. The correlation

St 1   St 2   St 3

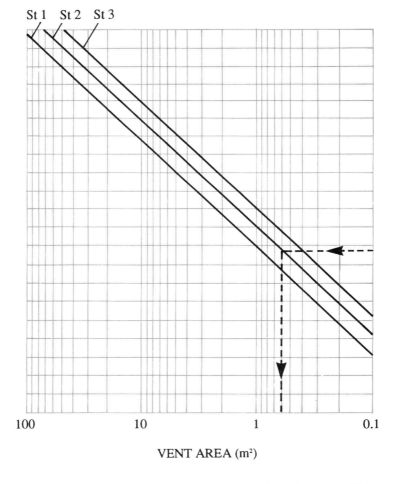

| 100 | 10 | 1 | 0.1 |

VENT AREA (m²)

Figure 4.5   Explosion relief venting: dusts. (From Guideline VDI 3673 (Fig 7 a – c). Printed with permission of the Verein Deutscher Ingenieure, Düsseldorf, Germany.)

limits of this equation are the same as the limits to the K_{st} nomographs:

$$2 \text{ bar g} > P_{red} > P_{stat} + 0.1 \text{ bar g}$$
$$0.5 \text{ bar g} > P_{stat} > 0.1 \text{ bar g}$$
$$600 > K_{st} > 10 \text{ bar m s}^{-1}$$
$$1000 \text{ m}^3 > V > 1 \text{ m}^3$$

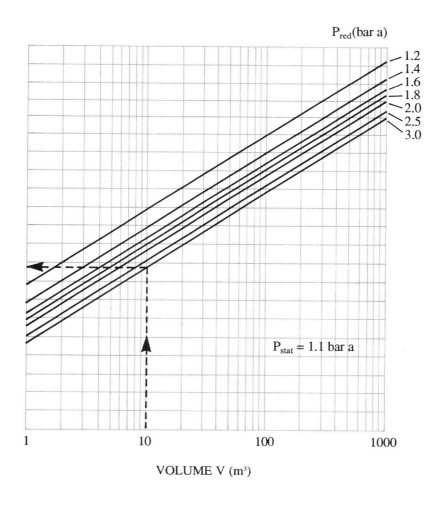

4.2   THE VENT RATIO METHOD

The vent ratio is defined as:

$$\text{Vent ratio} = \frac{\text{Area of vent}}{\text{Volume of the vessel}}$$

For many years in the UK and the USA vent areas have been determined using a vent ratio which is based on the maximum rate of pressure rise

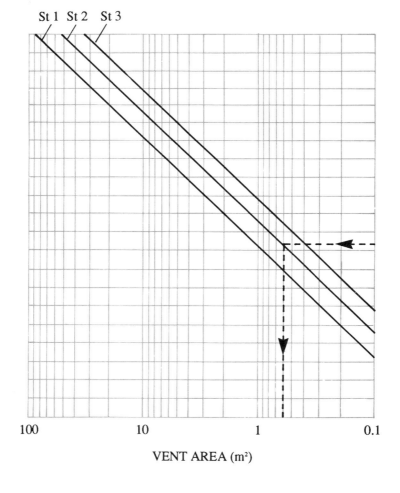

St 1 St 2 St 3

VENT AREA (m²)

Figure 4.6   Explosion relief venting: dusts. (From Guideline VDI 3673 (Fig 7 a – c). Printed with permission of the Verein Deutscher Ingenieure, Düsseldorf, Germany.)

measured in the Hartmann apparatus (see Section 3.2.1 on page 60). Data from the 20 litre sphere or 1 m³ test apparatus must not be used. For vessels up to about 30 m³ the recommended vent ratios are given in Table 4.1 on page 86. When the opening pressure and the inertia of the vent cover are low, and any vent duct is less than 3 m long, the recommended vent ratios are designed to limit the reduced explosion pressure, P_{red}, to 1.14 bar a.

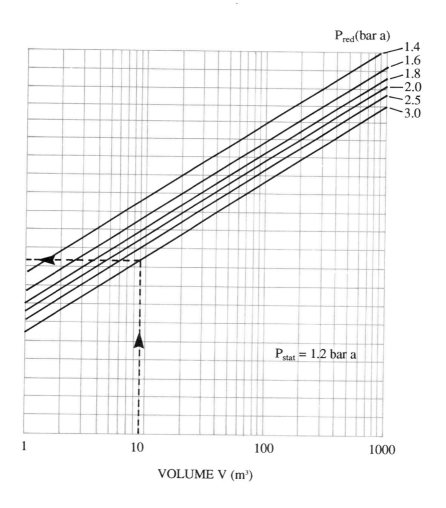

Because of the dimensional nature of the vent ratio, m^{-1}, the vent area becomes a greater proportion of the vessel surface as the volume increases. In large vessels the vent ratio figures in Table 4.1 produce such large vent areas that they become increasingly difficult to accommodate. The vent ratio can be reduced as vessel volume increases above 30 m^3 according to the recommendations shown in Figure 4.8 on page 86.

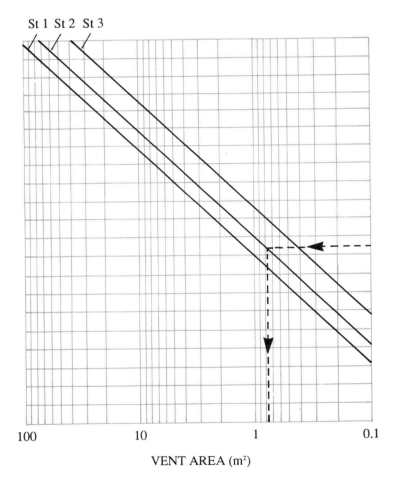

St 1 St 2 St 3

VENT AREA (m²)

Figure 4.7   Explosion relief venting: dusts. (From Guideline VDI 3673 (Fig 7 a – c). Printed with permission of the Verein Deutscher Ingenieure, Düsseldorf, Germany.)

This is the major criticism levelled against the vent ratio approach; that it provides for very large vent areas that can become costly if not impossible to fit. These large areas arise because the vent ratio method is based on a rapid flame propagation throughout the whole of the vessel volume rather than on a spherical flame front expanding from a single ignition source. Gibson and Harris[32] suggest that in most dust-handling situations such a high degree of

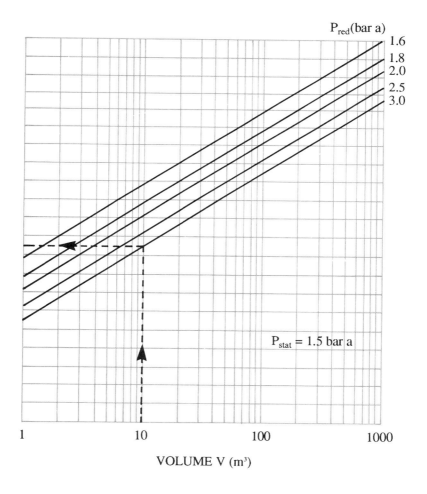

TABLE 4.1

Ratios for the vent area method for equipment volume up to 30 m^3

Maximum rate of pressure rise $(dP/dt)_{max}$ bar/s	Vent ratio $m^2/m^3 = m^{-1}$
< 350	1/6.1
350–700	1/4.6
> 700	1/3.1

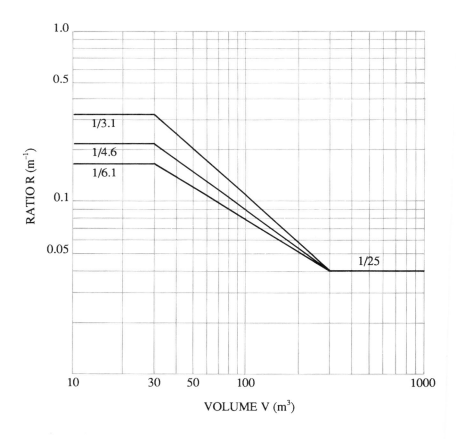

Figure 4.8   Vent ratio approach.

turbulence and fragmentation of the flame front is unlikely to occur throughout the whole of the vessel volume, and so the vent ratio could be expected to specify overlarge vent areas.

4.3 THE K FACTOR METHOD

The K factor method (not to be confused with the K_{st}) for estimating vent areas was devised by Cubbage and Simmonds[33] for gas explosions in drying ovens. It has been applied to dust explosions by Gibson and Harris[32]. Experiments showed that for compact rectangular vessels the maximum explosion pressure in a vented vessel was proportional to the ratio of the cross-sectional area of the vessel to the area of the explosion relief vent:

$$P_{max} \propto A_c/A_v$$

where A_c is the cross-sectional area of the vessel and A_v is the vent area. This ratio is designated K, so that

$$K = A_c/A_v$$

A_c is sometimes taken as the area of the side containing the vent but more often as the area of the smallest side of the vessel. This latter consideration means that elongated enclosures will be fitted with a lower vent area than cubical enclosures of the same volume. The reasoning behind this is that the area of a flame front approaching a vent along a cylindrical vessel will be less than one propagating spherically from a central ignition source in a cubical enclosure. However, experiments[28] have indicated that reduced explosion pressures in a silo ($L/D = 6.25$) are greater than in a cubical vessel with the same volume and same vent area, except when the vent area is relatively low and P_{red} consequently greater than 3 bar a. It is thus recommended that when the K factor has been calculated, the vent area be sized taking A_c as the area of one wall in a cubical vessel of the same volume as the vessel being considered, ie $K = V^{2/3}/A_v$. This vent area can then be introduced into any appropriate wall space.

For St 2 dusts the following empirical relationship linking the reduced explosion pressure, P_{red}, and K has been derived[32]:

$$P_{red} = 0.25\ K - 0.2\ \text{bar g}$$

This equation can be applied when the vent opens at a P_{stat} of 1.1 bar a, and the results agree reasonably well with those of Donat demonstrating that the nomograph method and K factor approach are closely equivalent.

The above equation can be rearranged to give the K factor as a function of P_{red}.

$$K = 0.8 + 4P_{red}$$

The K factor approach can be used:

- Especially for St 2 dusts in the absence of excessive turbulence;
- When the opening pressure of the vent cover is low and the inertia less than 10 kg/m²;
- When the vessel volume is between 1 and 1000 m³;
- When the vessel has a length to diameter ratio less than 5:1;
- When no vent ducts are fitted.

Generally this method gives a rapid means of estimating the vent area for St 2 dusts; but for greater precision the K_{st} nomograph method should be used.

4.4   WORKED EXAMPLES

4.4.1   THE K_{st} AND ST NOMOGRAPH APPROACH

The nomograph approach is applicable to compact vessels. It has been the usual practice to limit the length to diameter (L/D) ratio of the vessel to less than 5.

Four quantities need to be known in order to estimate the vent area by the nomograph method:

- The reduced explosion pressure P_{red}, which should not be exceeded and which depends on the strength of the vessel (bar a or bar g);
- The vessel volume (m³);
- The explosibility of the dust as determined by the K_{st} value (bar m s⁻¹);
- The static bursting pressure of the vent closure, P_{stat}, (bar a or bar g). Nomographs are published for three values of P_{stat}: 1.1 bar a, 1.2 bar a and 1.5 bar a.

EXAMPLE 1

A dust collector of 6 m³ capacity is used to handle a dust with K_{st} value of 150 bar m s⁻¹. The static opening pressure of the vent panel, P_{stat}, is set at 1.2 bar a (0.2 bar g). Estimate the vent area required to limit the reduced explosion pressure to 1.3 bar a (0.3 bar g), using the nomograph approach.

The appropriate nomograph is:

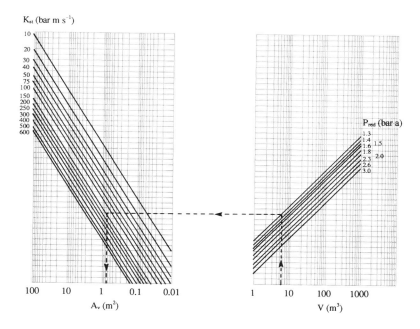

Following the arrows on the dashed line gives a vent area of 0.76 m².

Vent area = 0.76 m².

If the K_{st} value of the dust is not known precisely, a second set of nomographs can be used if an approximate value of the degree of explosibility can be estimated. Instead of differentiating between the K_{st} value in detail, these nomographs limit the number of lines in the left-hand side to three; one line for each dust explosibility group:

Group St 1: $0 < K_{st} < 200$ bar m s^{-1}
Group St 2: $200 < K_{st} < 300$ bar m s^{-1} Increasing explosion violence
Group St 3: $300 < K_{st}$

The dust in the example has a K_{st} value of 150 m s^{-1} and thus belongs to the St 1 group.

The appropriate nomograph is:

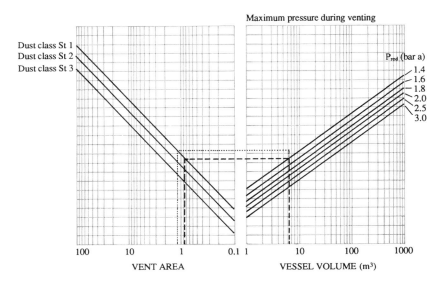

But when the arrows on the dashed line are followed, a problem occurs. This nomograph gives no guidance for values of P_{red} below 1.4 bar a. In the example, P_{red} must not exceed 1.3 bar a.

There is no problem in finding the vent area required to limit P_{red} to 1.4 bar a. The procedure is the same as before and the answer is 0.9 m². There can only be an extrapolation, however, to the vent area required to limit P_{red} to 1.3 bar a. Within the accuracy of the nomographs, the dotted line is more than satisfactory and the vent area is calculated to be 1.1 m². Both vent areas estimated from the St nomograph are in excess of the area estimated from the K_{st} nomograph.

Vent area = 1.1 m².

Simpson's regression analysis of the nomographs has led to the equation:

$$A_v / V^{2/3} = a \, K_{st}^b \, P_{red}^c$$

where a = 0.000571 exp [2 P_{stat}]
           b = 0.978 exp [−0.105 P_{stat}]
           c = −0.687 exp [0.226 P_{stat}]
with the units of P_{stat} and P_{red} in bar g.

So, using the data from the problem:
$a = 0.0008518$
$b = 0.9577$

$c = -0.7188$

$\therefore A_v / V^{2/3} = 0.0008518 \times 121.35/0.421 = 0.246$

$\therefore A_v = 0.246 \times 3.3 = 0.81$ m^2.

Vent area = 0.81 m^2.

4.4.2   THE K FACTOR APPROACH

Application of this vent sizing technique requires knowledge of the vessel dimensions.

If, as a first step, the equation

$$K = 0.8 + 4\ P_{red} = A_c/A_v$$

is used, (with P_{red} in bar g) then for an overpressure of 0.3 bar g, the K factor equals 2, ie $A_c/A_v = 2$, and the vent area, A_v, is equal to half of the wall area A_c.

If the 6 m^3 dust collector is cubical, the wall area equals $V^{2/3}$, 3.3 m^2, and the vent area equals 1.65 m^2. This value is much higher than the 0.7 m^2 calculated by the K_{st} nomograph approach. This difference follows because the K factor equation is applicable to St 2 dusts, and the dust in the example belongs to the St 1 group. If the dust in the example is changed to one with a K_{st} value of 300 bar m s^{-1} at the top of the St 2 range, then predictions from the nomographs can be obtained for a direct comparison with the K factor vent area derived above.

From the K_{st} nomograph used earlier with this example, the vent area would equal approximately 1.5 m^2; and from the St nomograph the vent area would equal approximately 1.8 m^2. Both of these values are in reasonable agreement with the vent area based on the K factor approach.

The K factor method can thus be used as a quick and easy means of assessing the vent area for St 2 dusts; but if the dust has a K_{st} value below 300 bar m s^{-1}, more accurate vent sizing can be achieved using the nomograph approach. The K factor approach can result in a reduction in vent area when the L/D ratio lengthens and some walls of the vessel have lower areas than the others, but it is recommended that A_c always be taken as $V^{2/3}$ and the appropriate vent area fitted into a suitable wall.

4.4.3   THE VENT RATIO APPROACH

Although the vent ratio method has been discussed in this chapter as a basic method, comparisons between it and other techniques are best made when discussing techniques for low strength equipment. These techniques are discussed in Chapter 5, and worked examples introduced there.

5. EXTENSIONS TO THE BASIC METHODS

In this chapter alternative methods for estimating vent area are described. These methods are similar to the nomograph approach and often based directly upon it, but they have been developed to provide a technique under circumstances where either the nomographs are not applicable or where the original nomographs are known to over-size vents.

5.1 VENT SIZING METHODS FOR LOW STRENGTH EQUIPMENT

The original St and K_{st} nomographs are limited to:

- Vent bursting pressures, P_{stat}, greater than 1.1 bar a;
- Reduced explosion pressures, P_{red}, greater than 1.2 bar a;
- K_{st} values greater than 10 bar m s^{-1} and less than 600 bar m s^{-1};
- Vessel volumes less than 1000 m^3.

The first two limitations are especially important because they render the nomograph approach unsuitable for low strength equipment. In the UK and USA, low strength dust-handling plant is widely used.

5.1.1 EXTENSION OF THE NOMOGRAPHS

Heinrich's model on which the K_{st} nomographs are based has been used to derive a simple means for estimating vent area when the reduced explosion pressure, P_{red}, is below 1.2 bar a[34]. A graph is given in Figure 5.1 which relates the reduced explosion pressure to the dimensionless vent area, $A_v/V^{2/3}$, where A_v is the vent area and V the total volume of the vessel. This graph is a direct extrapolation of the K_{st} nomographs using Heinrich's model. However, P_{stat} cannot be extrapolated directly and it is recommended that in the range of reduced explosion pressures 1.2 bar a > P_{red} > 1.05 bar a, the value of P_{stat} should not exceed[34]:

$$1 + \frac{(P_{red} - 1)}{2} \text{ bar a}$$

The restrictions on this method are:

- The inertia of the vent panel should be as low as possible, and at most 10 kg/m^2;
- The vessel volume should not exceed 1000 m^3;

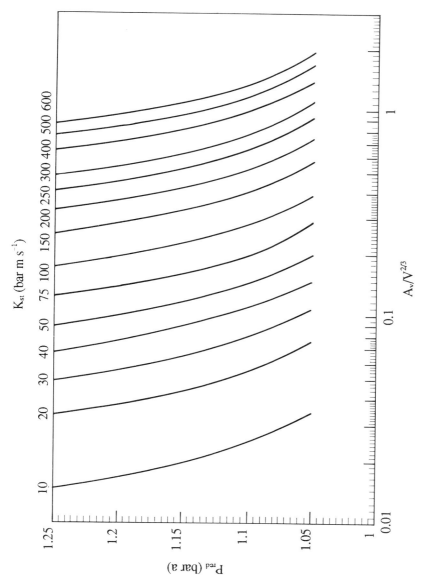

Figure 5.1   Nomograph: P_{red} (bar a) $\cong A_v/V^{2/3}$ for $1.20 > P_{red} > 1.05$ bar a.

- The length to diameter ratio should not exceed 5:1;
- Vent ducts are not taken into account.

A comparison between the predictions from this extended nomograph and predictions from Simpson's regression equation in Section 4.1.3 (see page 73) indicates that there is a reasonable agreement at reduced explosion pressure of 0.1 bar g and above, but below 0.1 bar g the regression equation gives a high value compared to the extended nomograph.

5.1.2   VENTING EQUATION FROM NFPA 68

A subsonic venting model for gas explosions[35] has been used to derive a simple venting equation for dusts which has been included in the National Fire Protection Association document No 68 (NFPA 68) on the venting of deflagrations[16].

This equation is:

$$A_v = C_1 A_s / (P_{red} - P_{oo})^{1/2} \tag{2}$$

where A_s is the total internal surface area of the enclosure, including floor and ceiling but excluding dividing walls, P_{red} is the reduced explosion pressure (psi), P_{oo} is the ambient pressure (psi), A_v is the vent area and C_1 is a factor which depends on the type of dust and has units of $(psi)^{1/2}$. The values of C_1 recommended in NFPA 68[16] are: 0.10 $(psi)^{1/2}$ for St 1 dusts, 0.12 $(psi)^{1/2}$ for St 2 dusts and 0.20 $(psi)^{1/2}$ for St 3 dusts. A comparison between calculations from equation (2) and the extended nomograph described in Section 5.1.2 indicates that the two methods predict equal vent areas for St 1 dusts, but that equation (2) predicts lower vent areas for St 2 and St 3 dusts.

Equation (2) is theoretically applicable to non-compact as well as compact enclosures.

Swift has suggested a value of 0.20 $(psi)^{1/2}$ for highly turbulent explosions of St 1 and St 2 dusts[36].

In NFPA 68, equation (2) is limited to values of reduced explosion pressure, P_{red}, no greater than 0.1 bar g, and P_{red} should exceed the vent relief pressure P_{stat}, by at least 0.025 bar g. Vent panels should release at as low an internal pressure as practicable: 0.01 bar g under normal conditions or 0.015 bar g in areas where wind suction may be a problem.

Equation (2) can be used up to P_{red} values of 0.2 bar g, and over the range of K_{st} values rather than with just the St groups if a suitable value of C_1 is inserted. A comparison of the extended nomograph (Section 5.1.1) and equation (2) produces the values of C_1 given in Table 5.1 which give agreement between equation (2) and the extended nomograph[37].

TABLE 5.1
Relation between K_{st} value and C_1 from equation (2)

K_{st} (bar m s^{-1})	C_1 (psi)$^{1/2}$
10	0.005
20	0.010
30	0.015
40	0.021
50	0.027
75	0.041
100	0.055
150	0.084
200	0.105
250	0.127
300	0.163
400	0.210
500	0.248
600	0.300

Vent openings should be spaced as evenly as possible over the available surface area of the enclosure. This is especially important for elongated enclosures where it would be wrong, for instance, to position all the vent area at one end. The application of this equation to elongated enclosures and to buildings is discussed in Sections 6.5.3 (page 132) and 7.7 (page 185) respectively.

5.2   MODIFICATIONS OF THE NOMOGRAPH METHOD

The vent areas predicted by the K_{st} and St nomographs are sometimes conservative, ie they predict larger vent areas than may be necessary. This conservatism is a result of several factors — the low value of P_{red} chosen as a design basis because of uncertainties as to the strength of the vessel, the high values of maximum explosion pressure, P_{max}, to which the nomographs apply, and the level of turbulence generated in the standard method of measuring K_{st} values.

In practice, many dusts have maximum explosion pressures less than 11 bar a. In some applications, the turbulence of the dust cloud prior to an explosion may be less than that simulated in the standard test, leading to lower rates of combustion, lower rates of pressure rise and thus to lower vent area requirements.

In such circumstances, venting requirements may be reduced. It is important, however, that before any departure from the basic methods is made, the evidence for and reasoning behind such a move are fully explored.

5.2.1   DUSTS WITH P_{max} VALUES LESS THAN 10 BAR A

The experimental evidence on which the original nomographs were based covered a number of dusts with P_{max} values ranging from 8 bar a to 13 bar a. These results indicate that, all other things being equal, P_{max} has an effect on the venting requirements. Some explosion tests in vessels up to 250 m³ in volume have formed the basis for some new nomographs published by Radandt[38] and which are applied to dusts with P_{max} values no greater than 10 bar a. The tests are described in References 39 and 40. The results show that extrapolation by the cubic law from measurements of reduced explosion pressures in small volumes (2.4 m³–25 m³) underestimates the values measured at large volumes (250 m³). An example of these results is shown in Figure 5.2, along with predictions from the VDI 3673 K_{st} nomographs. The measured reduced explosion pressures are below the predicted values, except for St 1 dusts in circumstances where the reduced explosion pressure exceeds 2.5 bar a. Figure 5.3, using data from Reference 39, shows how predicted vent areas compare with experimental measurements. For St 1 dusts and when P_{red} is at 2.5 bar a, the experimental measurement equals the predicted value when the vessel volume exceeds 250 m³.

The experimental results in these figures refer to dusts with maximum explosion pressures, P_{max}, of 10 bar a, while the predictions refer to maximum explosion pressures of 11 bar a. Bartknecht[40] and Radandt[38] presume that savings in vent area requirements can therefore be made for most industrial dusts and a set of nomographs has been derived from these results and are applicable for dusts with values of P_{max} not exceeding 10 bar a. These nomographs are reproduced in Figures 5.4 and 5.5 (see pages 98–101); in this text they are referred to as the Radandt nomographs. Note that these nomographs refer only to St 1 and St 2 groups and not to individual K_{st} values. Differences between the Radandt nomographs and the original St nomographs are greatest at low reduced explosion pressures.

In any practical situation, the safety factor required depends on the circumstances. There may well be an argument for lessening the venting

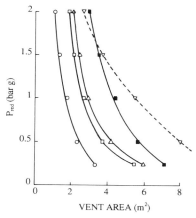

Figure 5.2   Cube root law conversion to 250 m³, and comparison with test results at 250 m³. K_{st} = 206 bar m s⁻¹. (Reproduced by permission of Dr-Ing S. Radandt.)

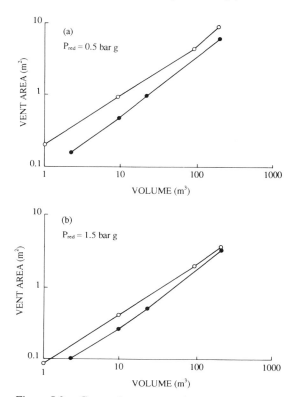

Figure 5.3   Comparison: test results versus VDI K_{st} nomograph predictions. P_{stat} = 0.1 bar g. (Reproduced by permission of Dr-Ing S. Radandt.)

97

Dust explosion class St 1

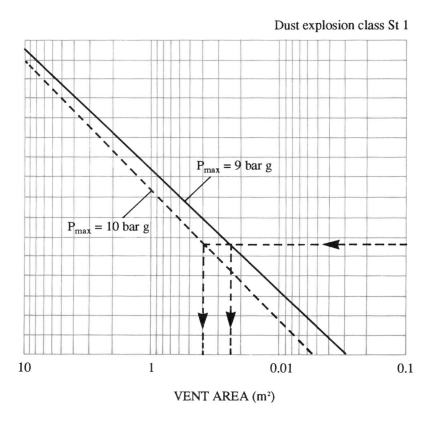

VENT AREA (m²)

Figure 5.4 Nomograph for dust explosion group St 1. (Reproduced by permission of Dr-Ing S. Radandt.)

requirements when the maximum explosion pressure of a dust is less than 10 bar a, but the Radandt nomographs are not as flexible as the K_{st} nomographs, and when the dust has a K_{st} value towards the lower end of the particular St group, the K_{st} nomographs will predict a lower vent area than the Radandt nomographs.

5.2.2 FORMULAE FOR THE ESTIMATION OF VENT AREAS

Formulae which act as alternatives to the nomographs have been published. NFPA 68[16] contains empirical equations which can be used as alternatives for the Radandt nomographs. For St 1 dusts:

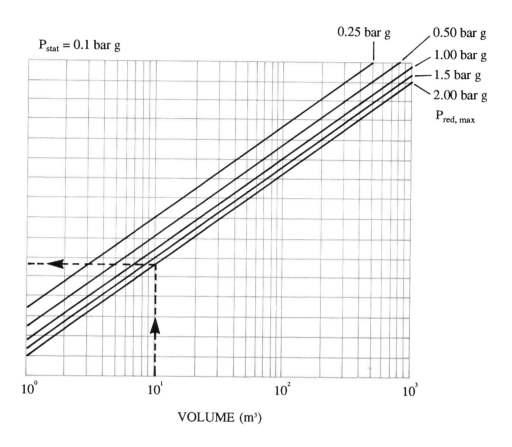

VOLUME (m³)

$$\text{Log } A_v = 0.77957 \text{ Log } V - 0.42945 \text{ Log } P_{red} - 1.24669$$

For St 2 dusts:

For $V = 1–10 \text{ m}^3$

$$\text{Log } A_v = 0.64256 \text{ Log } V - 0.46527 \text{ Log } P_{red} - 0.99461$$

For $V = 10–1000 \text{ m}^3$

$$\text{Log } A_v = 0.74461 \text{ Log } V - 0.50017 \text{ Log } (P_{red} + 0.18522) - 1.02406$$

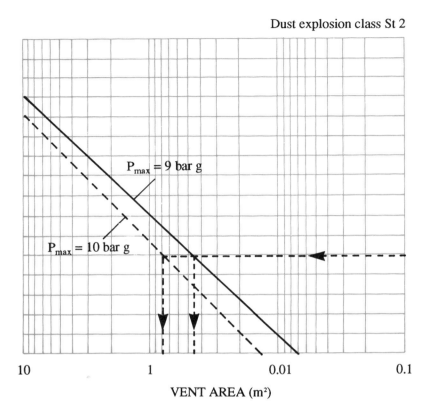

Figure 5.5   Nomograph for dust explosion group St 2. (Reproduced by permission of Dr-Ing S. Radandt.)

In these equations A_v is the vent area (m²), V is the vessel volume (m³), and P_{red} is the reduced explosion pressure (bar g). P_{stat} equals 0.1 bar g. These equations are a satisfactory simulation of the Radandt nomographs.

Scholl[41] has described an empirical equation for the determination of vent areas:

$$A_v = [3.264 \times 10^{-5} P_{max} K_{st} P_{red}^{-0.569} + 0.27 (P_{stat}^{-0.1})P_{red}^{-0.5}] V^{0.753}$$

where the various pressures are in units of bar g. It applies when $P_{max} \leq 9$ bar g for St 1 and St 2 dusts and $P_{max} \leq 12$ bar g for St 3 dusts; for vessel volumes between 0.1 m³ and 10 000 m³, for P_{stat} between 0.1 bar g and 1 bar g and P_{red} between 0.1 bar g and 2 bar g. The L/D ratio of the vessel should not exceed 2.

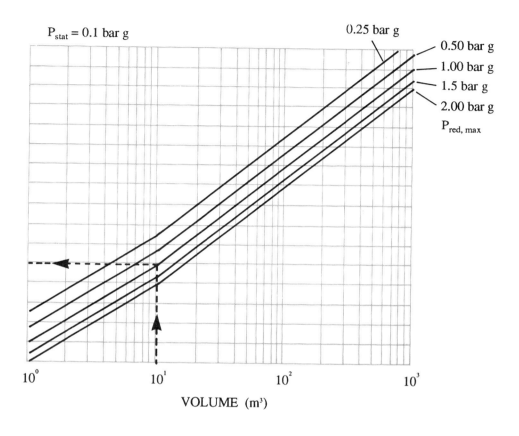

$P_{stat} = 0.1$ bar g

0.25 bar g

0.50 bar g

1.00 bar g

1.5 bar g

2.00 bar g

$P_{red, max}$

VOLUME (m³)

Validation of this equation is continuing but it is expected to be included in the new German VDI 3673 guidelines. It should be used, if at all, with extreme caution and with specialist help if necessary.

5.2.3   THE EFFECTS OF TURBULENCE AND THE AFNOR NOMOGRAPHS
The effect of cloud turbulence on the reduced explosion pressure of a vented explosion can be marked. The K_{st} nomographs, for instance, are based on dust explosibility measurements under conditions of turbulence that simulate on the small scale the conditions likely to be met with on the industrial scale.

A set of nomographs published by the French standards authority, AFNOR[42, 43] specifies the vent area for situations where the explosion could be very turbulent. An example of such an explosion would be a primary explosion in one vessel forcing a dusty atmosphere through an interconnecting pipe into an adjacent vessel, there causing a turbulent and possibly pressurized dust cloud, which is then ignited by a jet of flame from the pipe. The AFNOR nomographs are shown in Figures 5.6 to 5.8 (see pages 103–105).

The dusts are characterized by a parameter $K_{max\,t}$, essentially similar to the K_{st} value but measured under different standard conditions. The test vessel, developed by the French Safety Laboratories, INERIS (CERCHAR), has a volume of 1 m^3 and an L/D ratio of approximately 4. The vessel is shown diagrammatically in Figure 5.9 on page 106. The dust is injected through a nozzle close to one end, while the ignition source is close to the other end. The ignition delay after the start of injection is 0.1 s, which contrasts considerably with the delay of 0.6 s in a typical K_{st} measurement in the 1 m^3 vessel. The short delay means that conditions at the time of ignition are much more turbulent than in a K_{st} test and the explosion correspondingly more violent. The AFNOR nomographs refer to $K_{max\,t}$ values of 100 bar m s^{-1}, 400 bar m s^{-1} and 600 bar m s^{-1}, and to values of P_{stat} up to 1.2 bar a.

It is difficult to compare the AFNOR nomographs with the VDI nomographs because the relationship between $K_{max\,t}$ and K_{st} is not well defined, as Figure 5.10 on page 106 demonstrates. The situation is complicated because the optimum dust concentration when $K_{max\,t}$ and K_{st} are measured is usually not the same for the same dust. Generally, the concentration at which the highest rate of pressure rise is obtained is lower, for a given dust, in the French test vessel, and closer to the stoichiometric dust/air mixture.

The state of turbulence in industrial dust equipment is generally unknown. Until a systematic investigation of the turbulence generated in working plant is undertaken, the AFNOR nomographs should be used only when very high rates of turbulent burning can be truly expected both in the normal running of the equipment and in a likely incident, otherwise the predicted vent areas will be unnecessarily large.

The problem that confronts the users of vent-sizing nomographs is to specify a reliable safety margin. Whereas Radandt and others suggest that the safety margin of the K_{st} nomographs may be too high, the AFNOR nomographs pertain to circumstances in which it may not exist at all.

The development of these new nomographs is only part of the answer to this problem, because the state of the dust cloud in many industrial processes is not known. Although it is possible to divide industrial dust-handling equipment into several broad ranges of likely turbulence the actual circumstances of a dust explosion may render such a classification invalid. A relatively low turbulence dust cloud may become highly turbulent during an explosion because

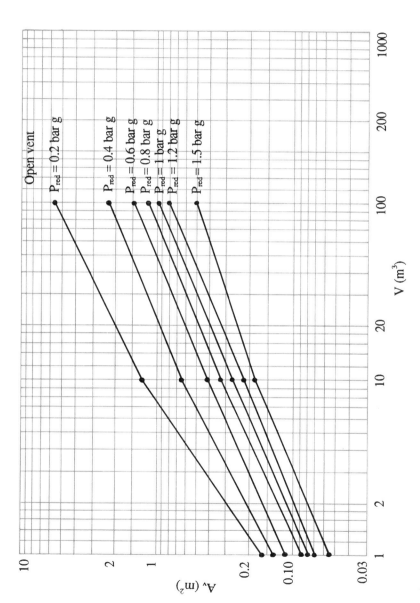

Figure 5.6   Vent area as a function of volume V of the vessel to be protected for different reduced explosion pressures P_{red}, with $P_{stat} \le 0.2$ bar, $K_{max\ t} = 100$ bar m s^{-1}. (Extracts from the French standard U54-540, December 1986, reproduced with permission from AFNOR.)

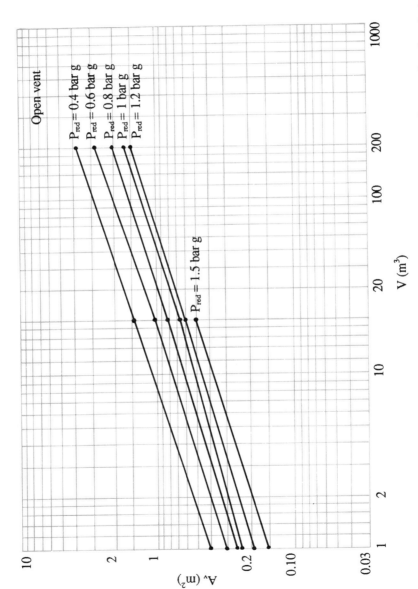

Figure 5.7 Vent area F as a function of volume V of the vessel to be protected for different reduced explosion pressures P_{red}, with $P_{stat} \leq 0.2$ bar, $K_{max\ t} = 400$ bar m s^{-1}. (Extracts from the French standard U54–540, December 1986, reproduced with permission from AFNOR.)

of a large ignition source, rapid gas movement and presence of obstacles. Eckhoff[44,45] considers that a differentiated approach to vent sizing may be required in the future, although this will require a great deal of experimental work using dust-handling equipment operating in a real situation and with explosions generated in credible circumstances. Until the problem of accurate vent area specification is resolved with adequate consideration of acceptable risk and shortcomings in test methods — one of which is a probable lack of correlation between different dusts when their explosion violence is measured by different methods and in different circumstances — the general nomographs and simple equations discussed in this chapter and the previous chapter remain the only practical methods of vent sizing.

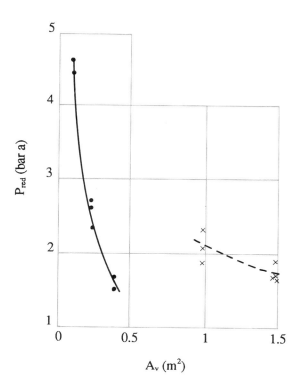

Figure 5.8   Reduced explosion pressure (P_{red}) as a funtion of the vent area with $K_{max\,t}$ = 600 bar m s^{-1} and $P_{stat} \leq 1.2$ bar a. (Extracts from the French standard U54–540, December 1986, reproduced with permission from AFNOR.)

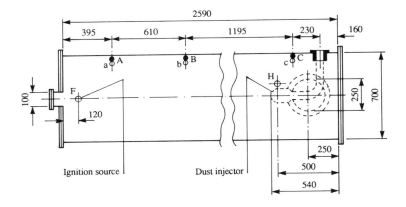

Figure 5.9   1 m³ explosion vessel (INERIS).
A, B, C — Pressure transducers. a, b, c — Flame detectors. (Extracts from the French standard U54–540, December 1986, reproduced with permission from AFNOR.)

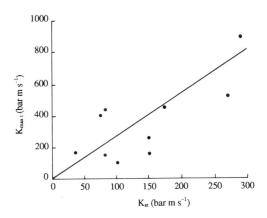

Figure 5.10   Relation between K_{st} and $K_{max\ t}$.

5.3 WORKED EXAMPLES

The worked example given in Chapter 4 (Example 1) and solved there using the K_{st} and St nomographs is solved in this chapter using the other methods described. The example is repeated below.

EXAMPLE 1

A dust collector of 6 m³ capacity is used to handle a dust with K_{st} value of 150 bar m s⁻¹. The static opening pressure of the vent panel, P_{stat}, is set at 1.2 bar a (0.2 bar g). Estimate the vent area required to limit the reduced explosion pressure to 1.30 bar a, (0.3 bar g) using the nomograph approach.

5.3.1 METHODS FOR USE WHEN P_{red} EXCEEDS 1.2 BAR A

5.3.1.1 THE RADANDT NOMOGRAPHS FOR A DUST WITH MAXIMUM EXPLOSION PRESSURE LESS THAN 10 BAR A (9 BAR G)

The appropriate figure is the St 1 group Radandt nomograph:

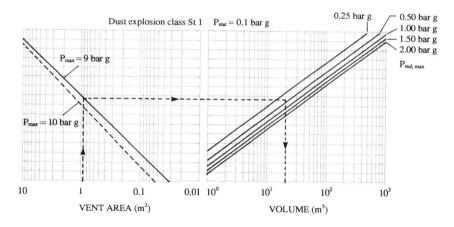

But this applies to a P_{stat} value of 1.1 bar a (0.1 bar g) whereas in the example P_{stat} is given as 1.2 bar a (0.2 bar g).

An approximate estimate of the vent area can be made by first finding an approximate ratio between the vent areas given by the St group nomograph and the Radandt nomograph.

Following the usual procedure, with the St 1 group nomographs:

A_v when P_{max} < 10 bar a (9 bar g) = 0.38 m²

A_v when P_{max} < 11 bar a (10 bar g) = 0.55 m²

The ratio between these vent areas is 0.7.

107

This ratio can then be applied to the results obtained from the 11 bar a nomographs obtained for this example in Chapter 4.

For an assessment based on the St group: **Vent area = 0.77 m².**

For an assessment based on the K_{st} value: **Vent area = 0.53 m².**

5.3.1.2 APPLICATION OF THE AFNOR NOMOGRAPHS

The nomographs applied up to now are to be used when the danger comes from a localized ignition source. In some circumstances, however, a flame propagating from one piece of equipment into another can act as a large ignition source of what could be a highly turbulent dust cloud. One option is to stop this propagation by means of isolation techniques; a second option is to design the venting requirements so that they can cope with the more violent explosion conditions. (Guidance on interconnected vessels is given in Chapter 7.)

The AFNOR nomographs may go some way towards assessing the venting requirements in these more violent conditions, but the explosibility of the dust should strictly be measured in the French INERIS (CERCHAR) apparatus if these nomographs are to be used. There is no precise relation between the explosibility measured in the INERIS apparatus and the explosibility measured in the 20 litre sphere.

For the purpose of this example, therefore, the explosibility measured in the INERIS test, $K_{max\,t}$, has been taken to be 375 bar m s^{-1}.

The appropriate nomograph is:

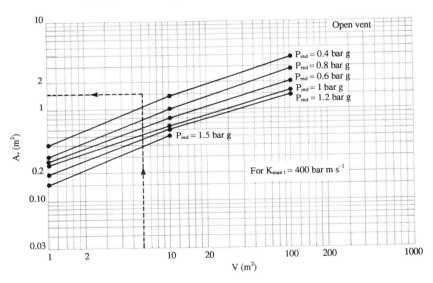

And reading from this nomograph, the vent area is 1.5 m².

Vent area = 1.5 m².

The vent areas predicted by the various methods for this example have been collected in Table 5.2.

TABLE 5.2
Vent area calculations for Example 1

Method	Vent area (m²)
P_{max} = 11 bar a — K_{st} nomograph	0.76
St nomograph	1.1
Regression equation	0.81
P_{max} = 10 bar a — K_{st} assessment	$\cong 0.53$
P_{max} = 10 bar a — St nomograph	$\cong 0.77$
AFNOR nomograph	1.5

Depending on the conditions expected, and the vent area calculation used, the vent area for this simple example lies between 0.53 m² and 1.5 m².

5.3.2   METHODS WHEN REDUCED EXPLOSION PRESSURE MUST BE
        LESS THAN 1.2 BAR A (0.2 BAR G)
The nomographs used up to now give no guidance when the reduced explosion pressure must not exceed 1.2 bar a (0.2 bar g). There are, however, some methods which can be used at these low pressures.

EXAMPLE 2
A vessel of 250 m³ capacity is used to handle dust with a K_{st} value of 250 bar m s⁻¹. The reduced explosion pressure must not exceed 1.14 bar a (0.14 bar g). Calculate the vent area necessary to limit the reduced explosion pressure to this value and specify a value for P_{stat}, the bursting pressure of the vent cover.

109

5.3.2.1   AN EXTENSION OF THE K_{st} NOMOGRAPHS
The graph is:

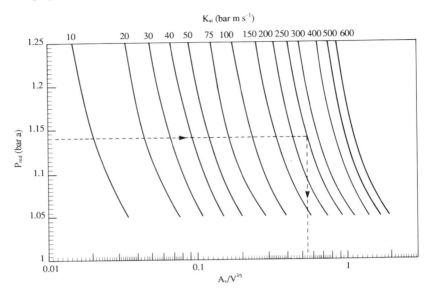

Following the dotted line gives a value for the dimensionless vent area,

$\frac{A_v}{V^{2/3}}$, of 0.53.

The vent area, A_v, $= 0.53 \times (250)^{2/3} = 21.0 \ m^2$.

There is no method for calculating the necessary P_{stat} value. It is recommended that P_{stat} (bar g) does not exceed P_{red} (bar g)/2.

And so, $P_{stat} = 1.07$ bar a (0.07 bar g).

Vent area $= 21.0 \ m^2$ and $P_{stat} = 0.07$ bar g.

5.3.2.2   VENTING EQUATION FROM NFPA 68
The venting equation is[16]:

$$A_v = C_1 A_s / (P_{red} - P_{oo})^{1/2}$$

The equation is suitable for non-compact enclosures and requires a calculation of A_s, the total surface area of the outer walls of the enclosure, including the floor area. Values of C_1 are specified for the St dust explosibility groups in NFPA 68[16].

In this example the equation will be used on a cubical and a near-cubical vessel. Its use with elongated vessels is demonstrated in Chapter 6, and with building-like structures in Chapter 7.

If the vessel is assumed to be cubical, the wall surface area, A_s, is $6V^{2/3} = 238$ m². For an St 2 dust, the recommended value of C_1 is 0.12 (psi)$^{1/2}$. The reduced explosion pressure is 0.14 bar g (2.06 psi g). Substituting the appropriate values into the equation gives:

$$A_v = 0.12 \times 238/(2.06)^{1/2} = 19.9 \text{ m}^2$$

Vent area = 19.9 m².

In order to demonstrate the application of this equation, the 250 m³ vessel is assumed to have a length to diameter (*L/D*) ratio of 3. The vessel, assumed to be cylindrical, has, therefore, a diameter of 4.73 m.

The total surface area is given by:

$$A_s = \frac{2\pi d^2}{4} + \pi d.3d = 3.5\pi d^2$$

where *d* is the vessel diameter.

$$A_s = 246.0 \text{ m}^2$$

For an St 2 dust, the recommended value of C_1 is 0.12 (psi)$^{1/2}$. The reduced explosion pressure, P_{red}, is 0.14 bar g (2.06 psi g). Substituting the appropriate values into the equation gives:

$$A_v = 0.12 \times 246/(2.06)^{1/2} = 29.5/1.435 = 20.6 \text{ m}^2$$

Vent area = 20.6 m².

This vent area should be compared to the value of 19.9 m² given for the cubical vessel. Elongating the vessel has increased the vent area required.

If the *K* factor approach (which is fully explained in Chapter 4) is applied to this example:

$$K = \frac{A_c}{A_v} = 0.8 + 4 \, P_{red}$$

where A_c is the area of the wall in which the vent is situated and P_{red} is in bar g, then:

$$K = 1.36$$

Thus, for a cubical vessel, $A_v = V^{2/3}/K = 250^{2/3}/K = 29.2$ m², and when the *L/D* ratio is 3, $A_v = A_c/K = 17.6$ m²$/K = 12.9$ m², assuming the vent is placed in the roof of the cylindrical vessel.

TABLE 5.3
Vent area calculations for Example 2

Method	Vent area (m^2)
Extended K_{st} nomograph	21.0
Venting equation from NFPA 68:	
Cubical vessel	19.9
When $L/D = 3$	20.6
K factor:	
Cubical	29.2
When $L/D = 3$	12.9

The vent areas predicted by the various methods for Example 2 have been collected in Table 5.3.

For cubical vessels, the venting equation from NFPA 68 has given the lowest value of vent area, even though the extended nomographs have been applied to a K_{st} value of 250 bar m s^{-1} while the equation is for the St 2 group. The K factor approach has produced the largest vent area; it too applies to the St 2 group. The effect of L/D ratio elongation has been best catered for by the NFPA 68 equation, but the K factor approach has produced a low vent area for the vessel when L/D ratio equals 3, and it is recommended that the vent area calculations for the cubical vessel should be used no matter what the elongation of the vessel is.

One other method which could, in principle, be applied to this example, is the vent ratio approach.

5.3.2.3   THE VENT RATIO APPROACH

The vent ratio approach (Section 4.2) cannot be used with dust explosibility measurements determined in the 20 litre sphere test (the K_{st} value); it was developed for Hartmann bomb data and there is, unfortunately, no straightforward relationship between measurements in the Hartmann device and the 20 litre sphere (see Chapter 3).

However, if the rate of pressure rise in the Hartmann apparatus is less than 500 bar s^{-1}, the dust can be considered as belonging to the St 1 group. Some St 1 dusts (as determined in the 20 litre sphere) can give rates of pressure rise greater than this value in the Hartmann apparatus.

TABLE 5.4
Vent ratios for vessels up to 30 m³

Maximum rate of pressure rise (Hartmann), bar/s	Vent ratio, $m^2/m^3 = m^{-1}$
< 350	1/6.1
350–700	1/4.6
> 700	1/3.1

The relationship between vent ratio and rate of pressure rise as measured in the Hartmann bomb is given in Table 5.4.

A dust with a K_{st} value of 250 bar m s⁻¹ is well into the range of explosibilities which require a vent ratio of 3.1 m⁻¹.

Furthermore, the vent ratio approach is strictly designed to provide a vent area which will limit the reduced explosion pressure to 1.14 bar a (0.14 bar g).

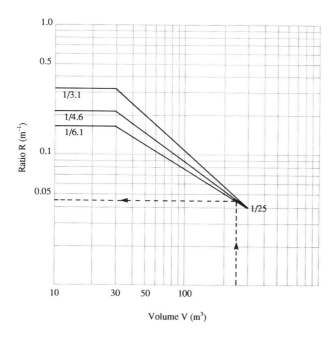

Using the vent ratio chart, and following the dotted line, produces a vent ratio of about 0.045, and the vent area, A_v, is given by: $0.045 \times 250 = 11.25$ m^2.

Vent area = 11.25 m^2.

This vent area is approximately half that obtained by previous methods of calculation. The reason for this disparity is that like is not being compared with like. The K_{st} value of 250 bar m s^{-1} is too high for the vent ratio to be applicable, and it has to be concluded that the vent ratio approach is not a satisfactory method for solving this example.

6. SPECIAL METHODS FOR DIFFERENT TYPES OF PLANT, INCLUDING PIPELINES AND SILOS, AND SITUATIONS INVOLVING PNEUMATIC FILLING

The previous two chapters have examined the basic methods of estimating vent areas for compact or near-compact enclosures. Variations on these basic methods, offering guidance where the basic methods do not apply, have also been discussed.

This chapter moves away from the basic methods, to examine vent area calculation techniques that can be applied to non-compact enclosures such as pipelines and silos. In addition, items of industrial plant for which there is some specific guidance available (eg drying ovens), are also discussed.

Firstly, however, the venting requirements for the special situation of pneumatic filling are described. In this situation the state of the dust cloud is different from the one created by the VDI dust injection technique described in Chapter 3, ie the turbulence is less and the cloud is not as homogeneous.

This discussion leads this chapter because the guidance is available for application to pneumatic filling of both compact vessels and silos.

Much of the guidance described in this chapter is not as well-founded as that discussed previously. It is often based on limited data and is not substantially validated. It should be used with caution, and the reasoning behind its application should be well-formulated. If necessary specialist advice should be sought.

Because of the uncertainties associated with this guidance, it has been allied in this chapter with some discussion of the research findings.

6.1   PNEUMATIC CHARGING OF VENTED VESSELS

In practice it is sometimes difficult to fit vents of sufficient area on some pieces of equipment. Criticism has been voiced that the state of the dust cloud in standard test vessels is not, as regards such factors as turbulence and homogeneity, the same as in some practical dust-handling equipment. Neither is the VDI method of injection, discussed in Chapter 3, typical of the way dust clouds can form in some circumstances.

Large-scale testing with dust clouds in a state of very low turbulence has been carried out, and some guidance offered as to the venting requirements in these situations.

Pneumatic charging of vented containers has been the focus of experiments by both Bartknecht[46] and Siwek[47] — the former in silo shaped containers, the latter in compact enclosures. Pneumatic filling was essentially the method used by Eckhoff to introduce dust into a 500 m³ silo[48], and constitutes flow of dust into a container through a single pipe entry as a jet of air and intermixed dust. In Eckhoff's experiments introduction of the jet was vertically upward, but in the later experiments[46,47], the jet was introduced vertically downward. In Siwek's experiments the air/dust was fed through a 90 mm diameter pipe positioned axially in the head of vessels ranging from 10 m³–250 m³ capacity. The ignition source, positioned at the vessel centre, had an energy content of 10 K Joules. The ignition delay was defined as the time between the start of dust feed into the containers and activation of the ignition source and was varied between 10–30 s without any noticeable trend being established vis-à-vis the results. The dusts ranged in K_{st} value from 73 bar m s^{-1} to 228 bar m s^{-1}.

The conclusions drawn from the pneumatic filling experiments can be applied to industrial practice only when the conditions match those of the investigation, ie:

• Pneumatic conveying is used;

• The fall height H of the dust in relation to the vessel volume either conforms to or is less than the data given in Figure 6.1;

• The container is approximately cubical;

• The feed is axially downward;

• The diameter of the feed pipe is less than 90 mm.

The maximum explosion effect is obtained at an optimum material-to-air loading of the dust stream. This is independent of vessel size and shape, size of the vent area and the air throughput, but it depends strongly on powder bulk

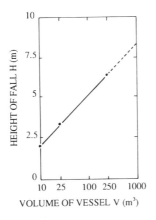

Figure 6.1   Pneumatic product feed into cubic containers: relation between the container volume V and the fall height H employed. (Reproduced by permission of the author.)

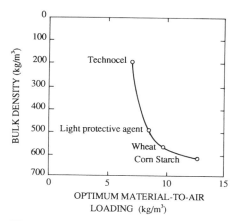

Figure 6.2   Pneumatic product feeding into cubic containers: relation between bulk density and optimum material to air loading of the throughput. (Reproduced by permission of the author.)

density as shown in Figure 6.2. The experimental optimum material-to-air loadings were obtained from plots of reduced explosion pressures and rates of pressure rise versus material-to-air loading under various experimental conditions; the curves were drawn through the maximum points obtained from a large number of experiments demonstrating a relatively large fluctuation for nominally identical conditions.

The air throughout Q (m^3/min) is an important variable and has an effect on the relationship between the reduced explosion pressure, P_{red}, and the vent area, as Figure 6.3 demonstrates.

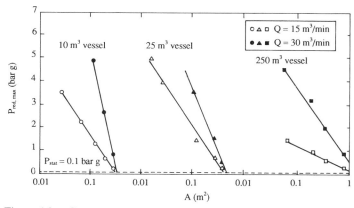

Figure 6.3   Cornstarch: reduced maximum explosion pressure $P_{red, max}$ as a function of the venting area A and the air quantity Q influence of the container volume. (Reproduced by permission of the author.)

117

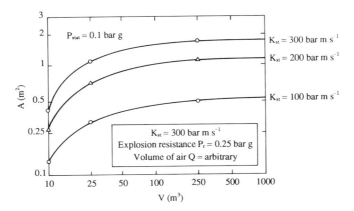

Figure 6.4   Direct pneumatic conveying of product into cubic containers: venting area A as a function of the container volume V for different dust-specific characteristics K_{st}. $P_{max} \leq 9$ bar g. (Reproduced by permission of the author.)

At low reduced explosion pressures, however, the effect of the air throughput, Q, on the vent area is minimal, and the relationship between vessel volume and vent area for dusts of various K_{st} values and P_{red} equal to 0.25 bar g is independent of Q, as Figure 6.4 shows.

When the reduced explosion pressure is relatively high, however, at 1 bar g or 2 bar g, a value of the air throughput, Q, has to be assigned. The data given in Figure 6.5 applies to values of Q equal to or less than 30 m³/min, this being the maximum air throughput used in the tests.

Figure 6.6 shows a comparison between these results and predictions from the K_{st} and Radandt nomographs.

The lower venting requirements which Figure 6.6 demonstrates are a result of lower turbulence than in the VDI injection method, inhomogeneities in the dust cloud and, especially when the vessel is of large volume, the volume of the cloud relative to the volume of the vessel. No attempt was made in these experiments to change either the diameter of the feed pipe or the ignition delay time as the vessel size increased. Increasing the throughput of air and maintaining the optimum material-air-loading by increasing the feed-pipe diameter would be expected to increase the size of the dust cloud in larger vessels and so produce higher reduced explosion pressures for a given vent area. It is more than likely that such a change in the feed conditions would mean that instead of reaching a constant value of vent area as vessel volume increases, the pneumatic

118

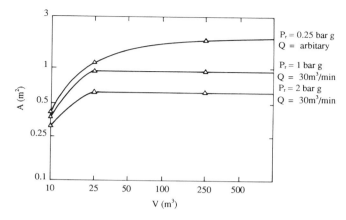

Figure 6.5   Pneumatic conveying of combustible products: venting area A as a function of the container volume V taking into account the container strength P, example: dust explosion class St 2. (Reproduced by permission of the author.)

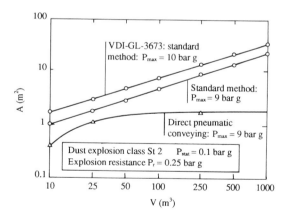

Figure 6.6   Explosion relief venting of combustible dusts: comparison of the area requirement in pneumatic conveying with the respective nomograms. (Reproduced by permission of the author.)

conveying data in Figure 6.6 would show a continual increase in vent area for increasing vessel volume, perhaps running parallel to the nomograph predictions. Furthermore, the L/D ratio of the vessel and the ignition position will both exert some influences on the reduced explosion pressure and venting requirements. It bears repeating that these results for pneumatic conveying are applicable as guidance only when practical conditions do not fall outside the range of experimental conditions used in the tests.

6.2 EQUATIONS FOR CALCULATING VENT AREAS WITH PNEUMATIC FILLING

Scholl[41] has described a set of equations developed to allow calculations of vent area for apparatus with pneumatic filling, when inhomogeneous clouds and only partial filling of the vessel by the cloud can be expected.

(1) For pneumatic filling of compact vessels (ie $L/D < 2$):

$$A_v = [(8.6 \log P_{red} - 6)1/D_Z - 5.5 \log P_{red} + 3.7] \, 0.011 \, K_{st} D_F \qquad (4)$$

where D_F is the diameter of the axial feed pipe into the vessel. The K_{st} value should not exceed 300 bar m s^{-1} and P_{max} should not exceed 9 bar g. The conveying velocity should not exceed 40 m/s. D_Z is calculated by the equation

$$D_Z = (4V/\pi)^{1/3}$$

where V is the vessel volume, which should be between 5 m^3 and 10 000 m^3. P_{red} should be between 0.1 bar g and 2 bar g, and P_{stat} should be 0.1 bar g. The height of the vessel should not exceed 10 m.

When the height of the vessel exceeds 10 m,

$$A_v = [(8.96 \log P_{red} - 6)1/D_Z - 5.5 \log P_{red} + 3.7] \, 0.0011 \, K_{st} L \, D_F \qquad (5)$$

(2) For elongated vessels (ie L/D ratio ≥ 2) an addition to the vent area is required:

$$A_{vL} = A_v + \Delta A$$

where A_v is the venting area for the cubical vessel with the same volume and ΔA the supplemental vent area when $L/D \geq 2$.

For homogeneous dust clouds (see Section 5.2.2 on page 98) as produced by the VDI injection technique,

$$\Delta A = A_v [-4.305 \log P_{red} + 0.758] \log (L/D) \qquad (6)$$

with P_{red} in bar g.

For inhomogeneous dust clouds

$$\Delta A = A_v \, 1.0715 \, P_{red}^{-1.27} \log (L/D) \qquad (7)$$

The pneumatic filling equations will only apply under a narrow range of conditions and should not be used to extrapolate beyond these conditions.

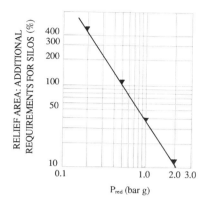

Figure 6.7   Some values of additional venting area for elongated vessels.
(Reproduced by permission of Dr-Ing S. Radandt.)

Figure 6.7 shows that some relief area enhancements can be large. This figure is used for illustration only and should not be used to calculate vent area additions for practical application.

The equations given in this section should be used, if at all, with extreme caution. They have little published validation and it is difficult to perceive a totally consistent picture. Validation is continuing, but it is expected that these equations will be included in the new German VDI 3673 guidelines.

6.3   VENTING OF DUST-CARRYING PIPELINES

A dust explosion can travel a long way if it is continually supplied with fuel. When confined by the walls of a duct or pipeline, an explosion can attain high flame speeds and generate high pressures. The process of propagation and acceleration depends on a complex interaction between the combustion processes of the dust particles, heat transfer, fluid dynamic phenomena such as dust dispersion, turbulence and pressure piling and the physical layout of the pipeline.

The confined combustion creates a gas flow in the pipeline into which the flame travels. Turbulence in the gas stream breaks up the flame front, increasing its area, accelerating the rate of combustion and leading to higher flow speeds and increased turbulence still. This positive feed back mechanism is a means by which the explosion can reach a very destructive potential.

A simple relation between the speed of a propagating explosion and the pressure it generates can be derived by approximating the flame front as a piston, which compresses a volume of unburnt gas ahead of it.

The final equation is:

$$(P_{expl} - P_o) = \rho_o C_o U_j$$

where P_{expl} is the explosion pressure, P_o is the ambient pressure, ρ_o the density of the unburnt gas at ambient conditions, C_o the velocity of sound in the unburnt gas and U_j the flame speed. This relation is known as the acoustic approximation[19].

With simple mathematics, the acoustic approximation demonstrates some aspects of flame behaviour. For instance, the higher the flame speed, the higher the pressures developed. If U_j is slow relative to C_o, the compression of the unburnt gas will move well ahead of the flame and can be vented through the open end of a pipeline. But as the difference between U_j and C_o diminishes, the volume of compressed gas ahead of the flame also diminishes, and because of the increasing confinement of the combustion process the higher the explosion pressures generated within it. When U_j equals and then exceeds C_o, the flame front overtakes the pressure front and a detonation is produced which travels at approaching the speed of sound in the burnt gas, $C_o(T_b/T_u)^{1/2}$, where (T_b/T_u) is the ratio of the burnt and unburnt gas temperatures. Pressures in excess of those produced in totally enclosed subsonic explosions can be developed in detonations because the confinement of the combustion process is so great. Detonations travel at supersonic speeds into the unburnt gas. Detonation or detonation type phenomena have been shown to develop in dust-carrying pipelines by Gardner *et al*[49]. Explosion pressure and flame speed measurements by Gardner are shown in Figure 6.8.

The results of Gardner's work demonstrate once again the importance of turbulence in the development of propagating explosions. In early tests, with an explosion propagating along 30 m of 0.6 m diameter unobstructed straight duct, flame speeds of 300 m/s were recorded, with pressures up to 2 bar a. But in later tests, with a 20 m³ explosion chamber connected to 40 m of duct and the explosion initiated in the vessel, the enhanced displacement velocities and the positive feed-back effect of turbulence on the combustion rate led in some cases to flame speeds of 2200 m/s and pressures as high as 33.3 bar. This order of flame speed has been measured in experimental mine explosions by Cybulski[50]. The highest pressure measured in Gardner's work was 81.5 bar, with a flame speed of 2850 m/s, using a coal containing 41.0% volatile matter. In this type of explosion there is a coincidence of the accelerating flame front with the peak of the pressure wave.

The protection of dust-carrying ducts and pipelines by explosion venting is described in NFPA 68[16], and the guidance offered therein is discussed in Reference 51. The NFPA 68 guidance is reproduced as Figures 6.9 to 6.12, and applies to pipelines operating at pressures up to 1.2 bar a. Figure 6.9 on page

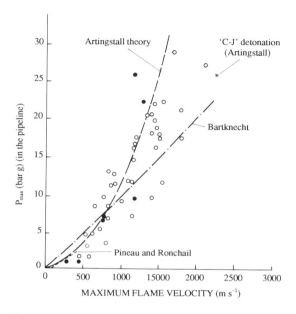

Figure 6.8   Maximum values of pressure versus flame velocity for phase 2 tests of two high volatile coals, size grade 250, compared with the findings of other investigators. (Reproduced by permission of The Combustion Institute.)

124 shows the maximum length to diameter ratio beyond which detonation or near detonation explosion conditions could occur. Figures 6.10 and 6.11 on pages 124 and 125 allow estimation of explosion overpressures in various circumstances, but always with the flow velocity less than 2 m/s, and Figure 6.12 on page 126 shows the vent spacing necessary to limit overpressures to 0.2 bar g when the flow velocity is between 2 m/s and 20 m/s.

The K factor approach (see Section 4.3 on page 87) has also been used to design the venting requirements of ducts. In order to limit the maximum explosion pressure to 0.14 bar g, Table 6.1 should be used[52] (see page 125).

For ducts containing bends or obstacles, extra vents are required near to either obstacle or bend.

The vent ratio approach (Section 4.2 — page 82) can also be used to calculate the venting requirements of pipelines. If vents equal in area to the cross-section of the pipe are used, they can be fitted at intervals given directly by Table 4.1 (see page 86), ie 6.1 m, 4.6 m or 3.1 m, depending on the values of $(dP/dt)_{max}$ as measured in the Hartmann bomb and given in Table 4.1. This spacing limits the reduced explosion pressure to 1.14 bar a (0.14 bar g). This vent spacing is independent of the duct diameter.

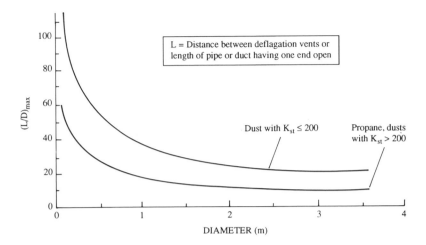

Figure 6.9 Maximum allowable distance, expressed as length to diameter ratio, for a smooth straight pipe or duct. (Reprinted with permission from NFPA 68, *Deflagration Venting*, Copyright © 1988, National Fire Protection Association, Quincy, MA 02269. This reprinted material is not the complete and official position of the National Fire Protection Association, on the referenced subject which is represented only by the standard in its entirety.)

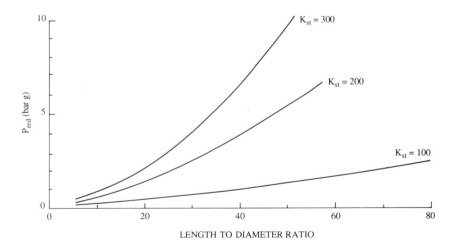

Figure 6.10 Maximum pressure developed during deflagration of dust/air mixtures flowing at 2 m/s or less in a smooth, straight pipe closed at one end. (Reprinted with permission from NFPA 68, *Deflagration Venting*, Copyright © 1988, National Fire Protection Association, Quincy, MA 02269. This reprinted material is not the complete and official position of the National Fire Protection Association, on the referenced subject which is represented only by the standard in its entirety.)

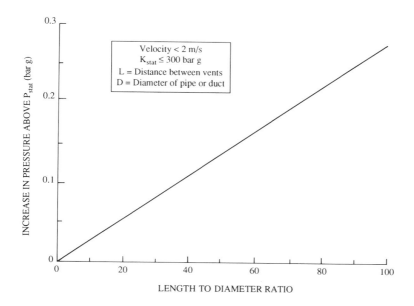

Figure 6.11 Maximum pressure developed during deflagration of dusts in a pipe or duct when more than one vent is provided. (Reprinted with permission from NFPA 68, *Deflagration Venting*, Copyright © 1988, National Fire Protection Association, Quincy, MA 02269. This reprinted material is not the complete and official position of the National Fire Protection Association, on the referenced subject which is represented only by the standard in its entirety.)

TABLE 6.1
K factors for venting of ducts (P_{red} = 0.14 bar g)

Duct diameter	K (ratio of cross-section of duct to area of vent)	L/D (ratio of distance between consecutive vents to hydraulic diameter of duct)
Up to 0.5 m	1	12
	2	6
0.5 m to 0.75 m	1	9
	2	5

125

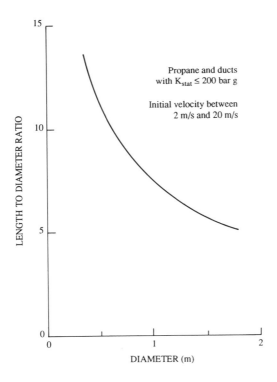

Figure 6.12   Vent spacing required to keep P_{red} from exceeding 0.2 bar ga.
(Reprinted with permission from NFPA 68, *Deflagration Venting*, Copyright © 1988,
National Fire Protection Association, Quincy, MA 02269. This reprinted material is
not the complete and official position of the National Fire Protection Association, on
the referenced subject which is represented only by the standard in its entirety.)

6.4   WORKED EXAMPLE

EXAMPLE 3
A ducting system is carrying an St 1 dust. Design a venting arrangement which
will limit the reduced explosion pressure, P_{red}, to 1.2 bar a (0.2 bar g). The duct
is 300 m in length, 0.5 m in diameter and the vent covers open at a P_{stat} of 1.1
bar a (0.1 bar g). The flow velocity is less than 2 m s^{-1}.

The first step is to find the maximum distance that is allowed between vents that will accomplish safe venting and prevent the occurrence of very high explosion pressures. This maximum allowable distance can be estimated from the appropriate graph, Figure 6.9:

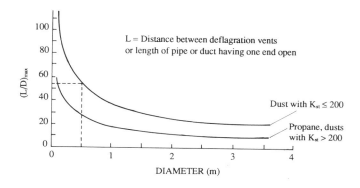

Following the dotted line:

The maximum allowable distance between vents (expressed as an *L/D* ratio) = 52, and the actual distance in metres = $0.5 \times 52 = 26$ m.

Next, the appropriate graph, one which relates the distance between vents (expressed as an *L/D* ratio) to the maximum pressure rise above the value of P_{stat}, is used to find the actual distance between vents that is required (Figure 6.11):

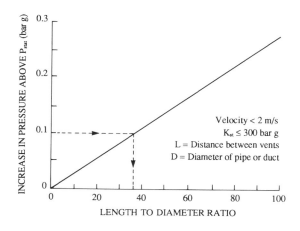

Following the dotted line:

The *L/D* ratio between vents of equal area to the duct cross-section necessary to limit the reduced explosion pressure in this example to 1.2 bar a (0.2 bar g) = 36 and this distance = 0.5 × 36 = 18.0 m. The actual vent spacing necessary is below the maximum allowable distance between vents.

The result shows that in order to limit the reduced explosion pressure to 1.2 bar a (0.2 bar g) at this low flow velocity, vents equal in area to the cross-sectional area of the pipeline should be positioned every 18 m, with venting areas at each end of the duct also.

If one end of the pipeline is closed, a much higher explosion pressure will be generated within a distance equivalent to an *L/D* ratio of 36.

From the appropriate graph, Figure 6.10:

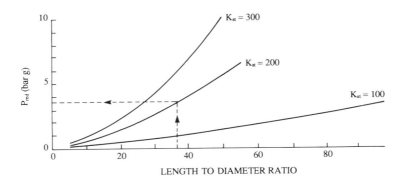

Following the dotted line:

The reduced explosion pressure would be 4.6 bar a (3.6 bar g) for a pipeline with an *L/D* ratio of 36, closed at one end and vented solely at the other.

The results of Gardner *et al* using coal dust showed that in a 0.6 m diameter unobstructed straight duct, 30 m long, explosion pressures up to 2 bar a were developed. Coal dust has a K_{st} usually between 100 bar m s^{-1} and 200 bar m s^{-1}. All things considered, the estimated pressures are reasonably close to the measured pressures.

If the flow rate through the pipeline lies between 2 m/s and 20 m/s, another procedure must be used. Using the appropriate graph, Figure 6.12, one

which relates the vent spacing necessary to limit P_{red} to 0.2 bar g to duct diameter:

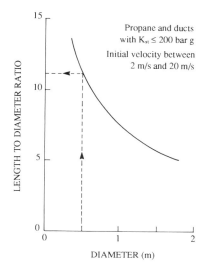

Following the dotted line:

The distance between vents of area equal to the duct cross-sectional area necessary to limit the reduced explosion pressure to 1.2 bar a (0.2 bar g) and expressed as an L/D ratio is equal to 16 and the actual distance in metres = $0.5 \times 16 = 8.0$ m.

This pipeline length is well below the value of 18 m obtained in the first part of this example.

This result shows that in order to limit the reduced explosion pressure to 1.2 bar a (0.2 bar g) at high flow velocities (but not exceeding 20 m/s), vents equal in area to the cross-section area of the pipeline should be positioned every 8.0 m, along with the venting area at each end of the duct.

Alternatively, the K factor approach suggests that for ducts up to 0.5 m in diameter, vents equal in area to the cross-section area of the duct should be positioned at L/D intervals equal to 12 if the reduced explosion pressure is to be limited to 0.14 bar g.

This estimate is reasonably close to the one derived from the guidance in NFPA 68.

Vents should be placed close to obstacles such as elbows, tees, orifices, valves and anything which blocks more than 5% of the duct cross-sectional area. Vents of area equal to that of the cross-section of the duct should be placed at 3 and 6 diameters each side of the obstacle. At junctions of dust-carrying ducts with vessels, vents should be placed within 2–3 diameters of the junction for St 1 and St 2 dusts if this is thought necessary. With St 3 dusts vents must be included at not more than 2 diameters distance of the junction.

6.5   VENTING OF SILOS

There are several methods for venting silos (length to diameter (*L/D*) ratio of 5 or more), none of which is wholly satisfactory. Explosions in silos can progress in very different ways depending on the method of dust injection and the position of the ignition source relative to the explosion vent. When it comes to applying the available guidance, users must be aware of its limitations.

6.5.1   GUIDANCE BASED ON ST NOMOGRAPHS

Methods for venting of elongated vessels with an *L/D* ratio in the region of 5 or greater have been specified by Bartknecht[7]. He suggests that the entire cross-section of the roof area should be used for explosion relief, and it is this area that defines the volume of the silo that can be protected. In new designs it is good practice to ensure that the roof area is free of equipment and that it is available for use as an explosion vent. By application of the basic nomograph approach guidance as to the maximum height of silo that can be protected for an St 1 dust at various reduced explosion pressures and silo diameters has been produced. This guidance is shown in Figure 6.13.

Below an *L/D* ratio of 5, the vessel is considered to be compact, the nomographs to apply without qualification, and vents can be placed anywhere where practicable on the vessel.

The maximum acceptable height of a silo according to nomograph calculations with the entire roof area used for venting is shown in Figure 6.14 as a function of silo diameter and dust St grouping.

6.5.2   RADANDT SILO NOMOGRAPHS

Radandt has developed a set of nomographs for the venting of silos, and these are reproduced in Figures 6.15 and 6.16 (pages 132 and 133). These nomographs have been derived from an extensive series of tests in horizontal and vertical silos with ignition either at the centre of the vessel or at a closed end remote from the roof vent[39]. The method of injection was by the VDI technique. The static burst pressure, P_{stat}, of the vent closure was 0.1 bar g. The nomograph guidance forms an envelope encompassing the most rigorous results in a 20 m³ silo.

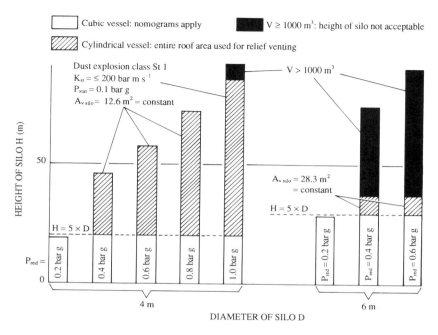

Figure 6.13   Dusts: influence of pressure resistance (ie P_{red}) of silos on the allowable height, by application of the nomograms.(Reproduced from Bartnecht, W., 1989, *Explosions. Course, prevention, protection* (Springer-Verlag) by permission of the author and publisher.)

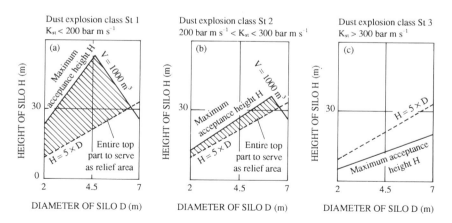

Figure 6.14   Influence of dust explosion class on the maximum acceptable height of silos, when the nomograms are used ($P_{stat} = 0.1$ bar, $P_{red} = 0.4$ bar).(Reproduced from Bartnecht, W., 1989, *Explosions. Course, prevention, protection* (Springer-Verlag) by permission of the author and publisher.)

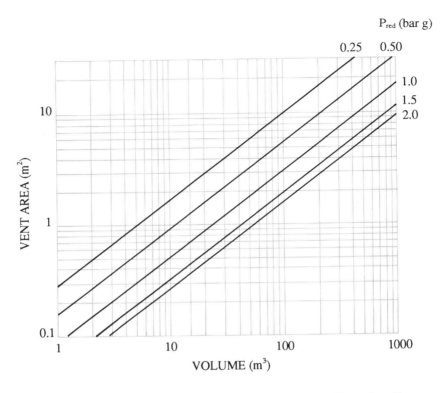

Figure 6.15 Venting nomographs for silos (Radandt) St 1 dusts. (Reproduced by permission of Dr-Ing S. Radandt.)

6.5.3 OTHER METHODS APPLICABLE TO VENTING OF SILOS

The NFPA 68 method for estimating the venting of dust-carrying pipelines (see Section 6.3 on page 121), and the general equation for venting of dust deflagrations given in NFPA 68 (see Section 5.1.2 on page 94), can both be used to estimate the venting requirements of silos.

The general equation from NFPA 68 is limited, however, to a length to diameter (L/D) ratio of 3 if the vent is limited to one end of the silo.

The procedure for using the NFPA 68 pipeline venting method with regard to silos is demonstrated in Section 6.6 on page 137.

6.5.4 DISCUSSION OF GUIDANCE AND ITS COMPARISON TO EXPERIMENTAL RESULTS

A comparison between the Radandt nomograph predictions and experimental measurements by Eckhoff is shown in Figure 6.17 on page 134. In these

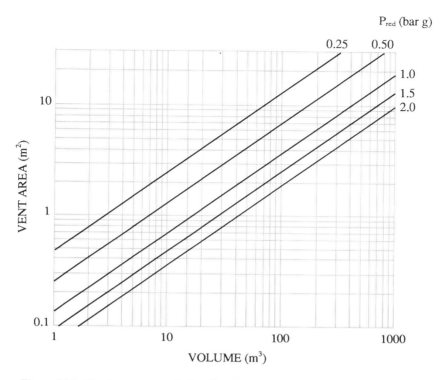

Figure 6.16   Venting nomographs for silos (Radandt) St 2 dusts. (Reproduced by permission of Dr-Ing S. Radandt.)

experiments the dust was fed through a 200 mm diameter pipe vertically upward into a 500 m^3 silo, with the dust cloud essentially quiescent at the moment of ignition. In one experiment, however, the cloud was ignited during the feeding process and the higher turbulence in the cloud has led to a much increased value for the reduced explosion pressure (point labelled 'turbulent jet').

Because Radandt's nomograph and the corresponding equation (Section 6.2 — page 120) are based on the VDI method of injection, predictions from them prove highly conservative compared to Eckhoff's experiments.

On the other hand, predictions from an equation for pneumatic filling of silos (see Section 6.2) produce a satisfactory envelope to Eckhoff's results. These latter calculations were performed assuming a P_{stat} of 0.1 bar g. The length of the silo was 20 m, the L/D ratio was 4.0, the K_{st} value of the dust 115 bar m s^{-1}, and the feed-pipe diameter 0.2 m.

Further experiments by Eckhoff, this time using a 236 m^3 silo[53], have demonstrated the difficulties that can arise if an overly simple view of explosions in silo-like vessels is taken. Figure 6.18 shows the effect that changes in the position of the ignition source along the silo axis can have on the reduced explosion pressure. The effect has not been great in some experiments by Radandt in a 20 m^3 silo using pneumatic filling, but has been significant in Eckhoff's experiments. Although both dust clouds were a result of pneumatic filling, Radandt ignited the cloud during the filling process, whereas Eckhoff ignited after filling was ended and the cloud was essentially quiescent.

Eckhoff's results can be explained if the reduced explosion pressure is taken to be a function of the time taken to burst the vent closure. When ignition

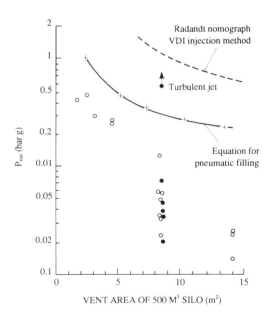

Figure 6.17 Results from vented maize starch and wheat grain dust explosions in a 500 m^3 silo in Norway. Comparison with predicted P_{red}/vent area correlations. Data from Eckhoff and Fuhre.

○ data from 500 m^3 silo, wheat grain dust.
● data from 500 m^3 silo, maize starch.
(Reproduced from *Journal of Loss Prevention in the Process Industries*, 1990, Vol. 3, p. 268, by permission of the publishers, Butterworth Heinemann Ltd. ©.)

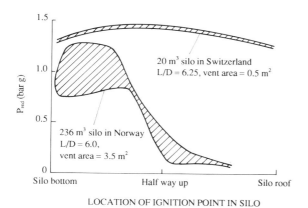

LOCATION OF IGNITION POINT IN SILO

Figure 6.18 Influence of location of the ignition point in the silo on maximum vented explosion pressure. Comparison of trends in a 20 m³ silo and a 236 m³ silo.
Reproduced from *Journal of Loss Prevention in the Process Industries*, 1990, Vol. 3, p. 268, by permission of the publishers, Butterworth Heinemann Ltd. ©.)

is at the silo bottom, the pressure rise necessary to burst the vent has to travel the length of the silo before venting can begin. As the ignition point is moved closer to the vent the localized pressure build-up is closer to the vent and it thus bursts earlier in the life of the explosion. Furthermore, ignition at the silo base leads to propagation towards an open end, with all the consequences for flame acceleration that that entails; ignition at the silo top leads to flame propagation away from an open end, a less serious case for flame acceleration as well as giving the added advantage of early venting of hot material. In Radandt's experiments, the relatively small size of the silo and the, presumably, greater turbulence in the dust cloud have meant that the more complicated behaviour has not developed.

The results from Eckhoff's 236 m³ silo experiments have been compared with predictions from the Radandt silo nomographs for injection by the VDI method. This comparison is shown in Figure 6.19 on page 136.

The first comparison in Figure 6.19 is between the 20 m³ experiments for a K_{st} of 100 bar m s⁻¹ and Radandt's prediction for a K_{st} of 200 bar m s⁻¹. The quantity A defines the difference between these two curves. The second comparison involves Radandt's prediction for a silo of 236 m³ and a dust of 200 bar m s⁻¹. This line has been moved to the left by A (which depends on the value of P_{red}) to give an estimate of vent sizes for 236 m³ and 100 bar m s⁻¹. This line is

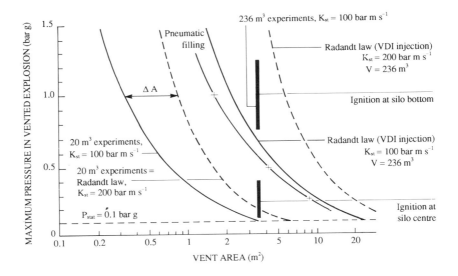

Figure 6.19 Comparison of Radandt's scaling law for silo vent sizing and experiments in a 236 m³ vented silo in Norway. Reproduced from *Journal of Loss Prevention in the Process Industries*, 1990, Vol. 3, p. 268, by permission of the publishers, Butterworth Heinemann Ltd. ©.)

then compared to the experimental results. The pressures generated by ignition at the silo base are above the prediction, those generated by ignition at the silo centre somewhat below. This has been adjudged as casting doubt on the scaling of the Radandt nomograph, although the St 2 line from Radandt's nomograph has satisfactorily encompassed the experimental pressures.

Similarly, the equation for pneumatic filling, assuming P_{stat} = 0.1 bar g, gives predictions which produce a satisfactory envelope of Eckhoff's results for ignition at the silo centre, but underestimate reduced explosion pressures for ignition occurring at the silo base.

It would appear from this discussion that the Radandt nomographs for venting of silos can be used to predict the venting requirements of silos, although the comparisons developed in Figure 6.19 imply that dusts with K_{st} values near the top of the St groups could develop higher than predicted pressures when ignition occurs at a point remote from the vent.

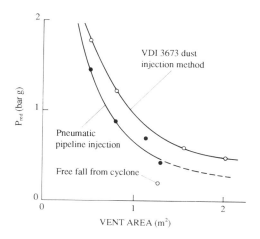

Figure 6.20   Results from vented maize starch explosions in a 20 m³ silo, demonstrating the marked influence of the mode of dust cloud generation on the maximum pressure. Data from Bartnecht[5, 30]. $K_{st} = 226$ bar m s⁻¹; $P_{stat} = 0.1$ bar g. (Reproduced from *Journal of Loss Prevention in the Process Industries*, 1990, Vol. 3, p. 268, by permission of the publishers, Butterworth Heinemann Ltd. ©.)

Finally, free fall from a cyclone into a silo can result in even lower venting requirements than for pneumatic filling, as experiments by Radandt and Bartknecht have shown[8], and as is illustrated in Figure 6.20.

Application of this information to practical installations is not easy. The conditions of dust feed, concentration of feed, point of feed, rate of feed, likely ignition sources and point of ignition need to be considered before an adequate assessment of vent sizes can be made.

6.6   WORKED EXAMPLE

A silo 18 m long, with a diameter of 3 m, is handling a dust with a K_{st} value equal to 175 bar m s⁻¹. If the entire roof area can act as a vent, what is the minimum strength of the vessel to be?

(a) NFPA 68 PIPELINE GUIDANCE

Because the vent is positioned in the roof of the silo, the first step is to ensure that the silo does not exceed the maximum allowable height. The length to diameter (*L/D*) ratio = 18/3 = 6, and from the appropriate figure, the maximum allowable *L/D* ratio for a diameter of 3 m and a dust with K_{st} 200 bar m s⁻¹ is approximately 20.

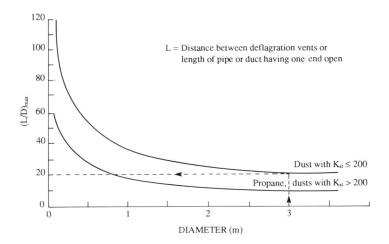

The silo *L/D* is therefore acceptable, and according to the appropriate figure, the reduced explosion pressure will be approximately 0.5 bar g.

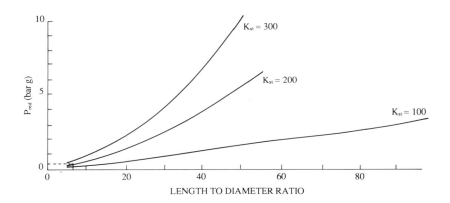

(b) RADANDT NOMOGRAPHS

The volume of the silo is 127 m^3 and the maximum vent area is 7.1 m^2. If the Radandt silo nomographs are applied to this problem the answer is again 0.5 bar g, approximately, as can be seen from the dotted line in the following nomograph.

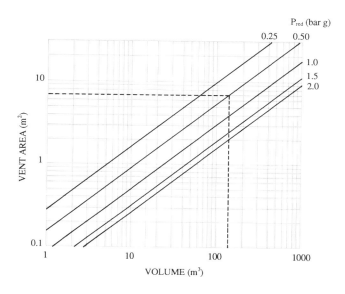

(c) GUIDANCE BASED ON ST NOMOGRAPHS

The guidance based on the St nomographs (Figure 6.14 — page 131) gives, for a diameter of 3 m and an St 1 dust, a maximum allowable height of silo of approximately 25 m when the P_{stat} value is 0.1 bar g and the reduced explosion pressure, P_{red}, is 0.4 bar g.

(d) VENTING EQUATIONS

Application of the pneumatic filling equation given in Section 6.2 (page 120) to this example is as follows.

If P_{stat} is taken as 0.1 bar g, then Equation (5) (Section 6.2) is applicable for a silo height of greater than 10 m. P_{red} is taken as 0.5 bar g.

$$A_v = [(8.96 \log P_{red} - 6) \times 1/D_Z - 5.5 \log P_{red} + 3.7] \, 0.0011 \, K_{st} \, L \, D_F$$

The volume of the vessel, V, = 128 m^3. $D_Z = (4V/\pi)^{1/3} = 5.46$. The diameter of the feed pipe, D_F, is assumed to be 0.09 m (90 mm).

Therefore,

$$A_v = [(8.96 \log 0.5 - 6) \times 1/5.46 - 5.5 \log 0.5 + 3.7] \, 0.0011 \times 175 \times$$
$$18 \times 0.09$$

$$A_v = (-8.69 \times 0.183 + 1.66 + 3.7) \, 0.31$$

139

$A_v = 1.17 \text{ m}^2$

To apply the supplement to the vent area because of the L/D ratio of 6 (Equation (7), Section 6.2);

$$\Delta A = A_v \, 1.0715 \, P_{red}^{-1.27} \log (L/D)$$

$$\Delta A = 1.17 \times 1.0715 \times 2.41 \times 0.778 = 2.35$$

Thus,

$$A_{vL} = A_v + \Delta A$$

$$A_{vL} = 1.17 + 2.35 = 3.52 \text{ m}^2$$

The vent area to limit the reduced explosion pressure to 0.5 bar g

$$A_v = 3.52 \text{ m}^2$$

The area of the silo top is 7.06 m². The equation for pneumatic transport has given a much reduced vent area (1.17 m²) compared to the other methods for a compact vessel, but because of the L/D ratio the final vent area is approximately half the value when a homogeneous dust cloud is assumed. These differences demonstrate the importance of making sure that the calculation method used is fully appropriate to the conditions of the dust handling process.

To round off these calculations of silo venting requirements, the vent area supplement method Scholl[41] has described for homogeneous dust clouds will be used. The equation for vent areas in compact enclosures is given in Section 5.2.2 (page 98):

$$A_v = [3.264 \times 10^{-5} P_{max} \, K_{st} \, P_{red}^{-0.569} + 0.27 \, (P_{stat} - 0.1) \, P_{red}^{-0.5}] \, V^{0.753}$$

For $P_{max} = 9$ bar g, $K_{st} = 175$ bar m s^{-1}, $P_{stat} = 0.1$ bar g, $V = 128$ m³ and $P_{red} = 0.5$ bar g:

$$A_v = [0.076] \, 38.6 = 2.93 \text{ m}^2$$

The vent area supplement for L/D ratios greater than 2, and for homogeneous dust clouds, is given by Equation (6) in Section 6.2.

$$\Delta A = A_v \, [-4.305 \log P_{red} + 0.758] \log (L/D)$$

and, with $L/D = 6$,

$$\Delta A = 2.93 \, [2.054] \, 0.778 = 4.68$$

Thus, the vent area $= 4.68 + 2.93 = 7.61 \text{ m}^2$.

This value is approximately the same as given by the Radandt silo nomographs and other methods.

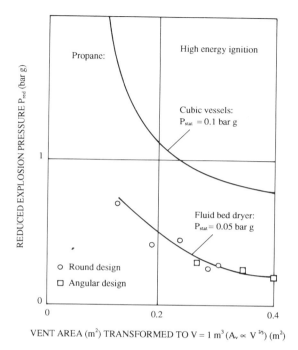

Figure 6.21   Propane-gas venting nomograph high energy ignition source.
(Reproduced from Bartnecht, W., 1989, *Explosions. Course, prevention, protection*
(Springer-Verlag) by permission of the author and publisher.)

These equations are still undergoing validation. It is expected that they
will be included in the new German VDI 3673 guidelines, but they should be
used with caution and with specialist help if necessary.

6.7   VENTING OF FLUID BED UNITS

Normally the K_{st} nomograph approach (Chapter 4) gives an adequate assessment
of vent area. If mixtures of dust and flammable gas — so called hybrid mixtures
(see Section 2.2.1.1 on page 22) — are likely to be present, the graph showing
relief area data for propane with a high energy ignition source in Figure 6.21
should be used.

141

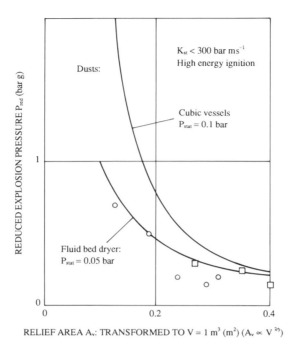

REDUCED EXPLOSION PRESSURE P_{red} (bar g)

Dusts:

$K_{st} < 300$ bar ms^{-1}
High energy ignition

Cubic vessels
$P_{stat} = 0.1$ bar

Fluid bed dryer:
$P_{stat} = 0.05$ bar

RELIEF AREA A_v: TRANSFORMED TO V = 1 m^3 (m^2) ($A_v \propto V^{2/3}$)

Figure 6.22   Venting information for fluid bed dryers up to 6 m^3 in volume. (Reproduced from Bartnecht, W., 1989, *Explosions. Course, prevention, protection* (Springer-Verlag) by permission of the author and publisher.)

Bartknecht has shown experimentally, however, that for batch fluid bed driers up to 6 m^3 volume, and when $P_{stat} = 0.05$ bar g, the nomograph approach to vent sizing gives conservative values[7]. Bartknecht recommends that the experimental data given in Figure 6.22 be used when relief areas are positioned on the product side of the filter. Vent areas for any particular plant volume are obtained by applying the cube root law to the vent areas read off the graphs.

In these special circumstances, and when hybrid mixtures are present, the propane nomograph for a weak ignition source is recommended for vent area calculations. This nomograph is given in Figure 6.23.

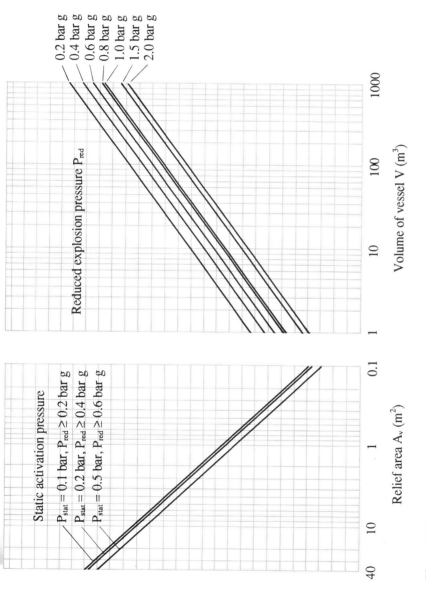

Figure 6.23   Venting nomographs for propane (weak ignition source). Propane, solvent vapours: $K_G = 75$ bar m s^{-1}, weak ignition source, ignition at zero turbulence.   (Reproduced from Bartnecht, W.., 1989, *Explosions. Course, prevention, protection* (Springer-Verlag) by permission of the author and publisher.)

143

Bartknecht provides further guidance for these special circumstances:
- With vent ducts less than 3 m in length ((a) — propane, (b) — combustible dusts: $K_{st} \leq 300$ bar m s^{-1}).

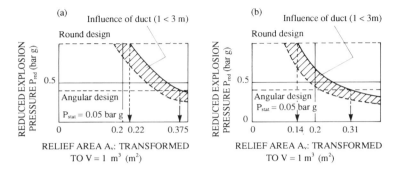

Relief areas A_v for dryers and granulators with a volume V, when vented on product side of filter (pressure shock resistance $P_D = 1$ bar, length of duct $1 < 3$ m).

Shape	K_{st} (bar m s^{-1})	A_v (m^2)
Square	≤ 300 no solvents present	$0.31\ V^{2/3}$
	≤ 300 solvents present	$0.38\ V^{2/3}$
Round	≤ 300 no solvents present	$0.14\ V^{2/3}$
	≤ 300 solvents present	$0.22\ V^{2/3}$

- With vent ducts less than 6 m in length.

Relief area A_v for dryers and granulators with a volume V and relief venting on product side of filter (pressure shock resistance $P_D = 1$ bar, length of relief pipe $1 \leq 6$ m).

Shape	K_{st} (bar m s^{-1})	A_v (m^2)
Round	≤ 300 no solvents present	$0.18\ V^{2/3}$
	≤ 300 solvents present	$0.27\ V^{2/3}$

- Venting on the clean side of the filter:
— without relief ducts;

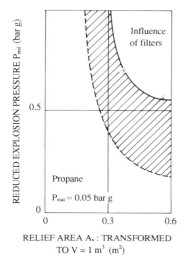

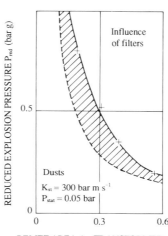

RELIEF AREA A$_v$: TRANSFORMED
TO V = 1 m^3 (m^2)

RELIEF AREA A$_v$: TRANSFORMED
TO V = 1 m^3 (m^2)

— with relief ducts.

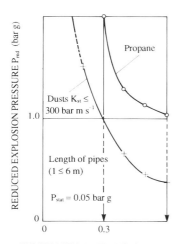

RELIEF AREA A$_v$: TRANSFORMED
TO V = 1 m^3 (m^2)

Relief areas A_v for dryers and granulators with a volume V for venting on clean side of filter (pressure shock resistance $P_D = 2$ bar, length of relief line $1 < 6$ m).

Shape	K_{st} (bar m s^{-1})	A_v (m^2)
Round	≤ 300 no solvents present	$0.3\ V^{2/3}$
	≤ 300 solvents present	$0.6\ V^{2/3}$

The volume of the dryer should be no greater than 6 m^3 and the filters should be of the unsupported type. These results are from measurements in one particular type of dryer. The data should not be used unless it is certain that in the event of an explosion the filter bags cannot block the movement of the flame towards the vent.

For venting on the clean side of the filter, the pressure shock resistance should be 2 bar g, and for safety reasons the venting designed as if the pressure shock resistance was 1 bar g.

6.8   VENTING OF OTHER ITEMS OF DUST-HANDLING EQUIPMENT

The guidance in this section refers to explosions ignited within the unit itself and not from flame propagation into the unit. The venting of interconnected units is discussed in Section 6.9 on page 153. Precautions against the transmission of explosion from one item of plant to another must be taken in all the following units.

6.8.1   RECOVERY CYCLONES

Cyclones require venting. Most cyclones are of relatively weak construction and are outside the range of the K_{st} nomographs given in Chapter 4. The methods for low-strength equipment are applicable but can be expected to give conservative answers when the full volume is used. Experiments under realistic conditions show that explosion pressures in vented cyclones can be very low[54], and for organic dusts in the St 1 group, Eckhoff[55] has suggested that vent areas can be reduced relative to the predictions from the original nomographs. However, normal predictive methods should be used, unless a sufficient case can be made for reducing the vent area.

The most favourable position for the vents is on the top surface of the cyclone body. Sometimes they can be positioned on top of the vortex tube but

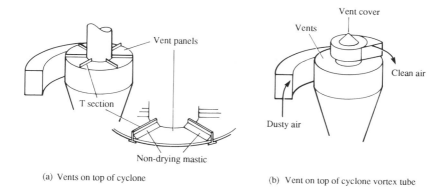

Figure 6.24   Venting arrangements on a cyclone.

explosion pressures will, as a consequence, be higher and the vortex tube must be strong enough to withstand the explosion. Figure 6.24 demonstrates diagrammatically some possible venting arrangements.

6.8.2   THE DUST FILTER/SEPARATOR

The nomograph approach (Chapter 4) will give a satisfactory value for the vent area. Venting should always be placed on the dirty side, as close to the likely ignition source as possible. Filter elements should not obstruct the vent area unless this obstruction has been taken into account in sizing the vent. If possible the flame should have an unobstructed passage to the vent opening. Much lower reduced explosion pressures are generated if the flame does not have to pass through the racks of filters before reaching the vent. Realistic experiments in bag filters reveal lower reduced explosion pressures than predicted by the original nomographs[56], and Eckhoff has suggested that the vent area can be reduced relative to the predicted value when the ignition source is inside the filter[55]. However, it is best to use the K_{st} or St nomographs procedure, unless a sufficient case can be made for reducing the vent area.

When sizing vent openings in a filter the free volume of the enclosure should be used (ie excluding bags), and not the total volume.

If the clean side volume is greater than half the dirty side volume it is prudent to provide the clean side with vents in case dust deposits have built up over time and are capable of being stirred up by an explosion. A typical filter is

147

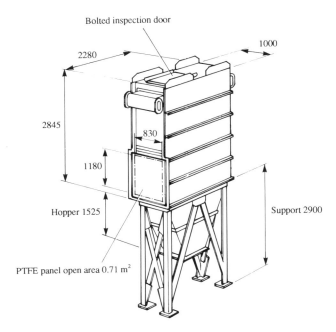

Figure 6.25 Vented dust filter/separator.

shown in Figure 6.25. Most filters can withstand an overpressure of 0.7 bar g. Vent sizing should be based on a value for P_{red} of 0.35 bar g or less.

6.8.3   SPRAY DRYERS

The K_{st} nomograph method (Chapter 4) provides adequate vent area estimation when the L/D ratio of the dryer is less than 5. It has been argued that the nomographs are considered to be conservative both because of the large volumes usual with this kind of plant and because the explosible dust cloud does not normally fill the vessel, but is generally considered to occupy the lower third of the volume.

However, this is not a sufficient reason for relaxing the venting requirements because in the event of an explosion dust deposited on the walls of the dryer can be disturbed and so fuel the explosion. The total volume must be used in the vent sizing procedure, unless specialist advise indicates otherwise. An acceptable and detailed case must be made if a volume less than the total volume is used for the vent sizing method.

When hybrid mixtures of flammable gas and explosible dust are present in the dryer then the appropriate nomograph for estimating vent areas for propane explosions must be used.

A basic design of spray drier is shown in Figure 6.26. The design strength of spray driers is usually in the region of 0.2 bar g, rarely rising above 0.4 bar g.

Venting of other types of drier — pneumatic, rotary and band driers — is discussed in the IChemE guide, *Prevention of fires and explosions in driers*[15].

6.8.4   GRINDERS AND MILLS

Venting is not usually applicable to grinders, which are generally built strong enough to withstand the explosion, but attached items of equipment such as collecting hoppers need venting by an appropriate method. Because of the grinding tools, grinders have an enlarged inner surface area and the explosion pressure and rate of pressure rise are often reduced compared to what would be expected in an empty compact vessel. Air inlet and dust discharge openings may act as sufficient inherent venting for mills and grinders, but the attachment of ducts to the former will increase the explosion pressure and the danger of

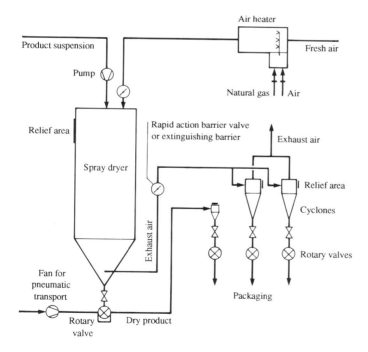

Figure 6.26   Basic design of spray dryer.

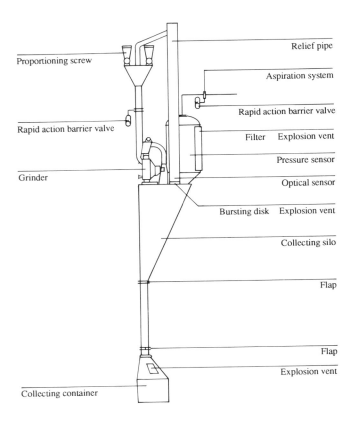

Relief pipe

Proportioning screw

Aspiration system

Rapid action barrier valve

Rapid action barrier valve

Filter   Explosion vent

Pressure sensor

Grinder

Optical sensor

Bursting disk   Explosion vent

Collecting silo

Flap

Flap

Explosion vent

Collecting container

Figure 6.27   Grinding installation protected by explosion relief venting. (Reproduced from Bartnecht, W., 1989, *Explosions. Course, prevention, protection* (Springer-Verlag) by permission of the author and publisher.)

explosion propagation into other parts of the plant must not be overlooked. If venting of mills is possible, Eckhoff[55] suggests that the basic nomograph method (Chapter 4) be used. It is recommended[57] that an installation such as the one in Figure 6.27 should be designed for at least 2–3 bar g, with isolation techniques applied to the feed side and air exhaust.

6.8.5   ELEVATORS

Bucket elevators are essentially formed of two lengths of duct with the additional complication that they are partially obstructed. Figure 6.28 demonstrates the position of explosion venting relief. The vent areas — equal in cross-section

150

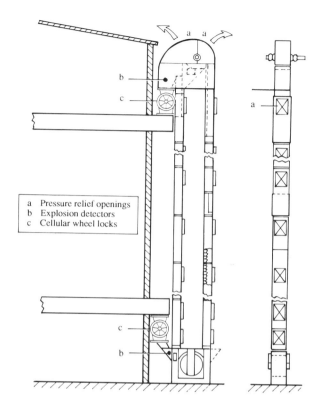

a Pressure relief openings
b Explosion detectors
c Cellular wheel locks

Figure 6.28   Protected elevator with pressure relief (explosion isolation with cellular wheel lock).

area to the limb cross-section — are positioned according to the guidance for ducting (see Section 6.3 on page 121) or, alternatively, a spacing between vents of 6 m is used. The top casing and boot must also be explosion relieved according to any of the basic methods. When there are no devices such as rotary valves which can act as a barrier to the passage of the explosion from the bucket elevator to the dust feed system, the feed system itself must be adequately protected against explosion.

6.8.6   VENTING OF STORAGE BINS

For storage bins vent areas should be sized according to the usual methods, as in Figure 6.29 on page 152, where a vent sized for $P_{stat} = 0.2$ bar g, $P_{red} = 0.4$ bar g and an St 1 group dust has been fitted. The storage bin shown in Figure 6.29 is similar to one in which an explosion was successfully vented[58].

151

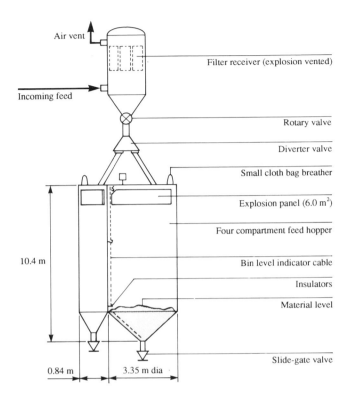

Figure 6.29   Feed hopper system. (Reproduced from 'Analysis of a dust deflagration', by Laurence G. Britton and David C. Kirby, *Plant/Operations Progress*, Vol. 8, No. 3, pp. 177–180 (1989) by permission of the American Institute of Chemical Engineers © 1989 AIChE.)

6.8.7   VENTING OF POWDER BLENDERS
Where protection is necessary, vent areas should be calculated by means of the basic methods. The blending motion must be stopped immediately once a vent is activated otherwise larger dust clouds may be generated.

Rotating blenders cannot be vented and alternative methods of protection are difficult to apply. Special care must be taken to exclude all ignition sources during operation and during loading.

6.8.8   EQUIPMENT THAT IS DIFFICULT TO VENT
Some grinding, screening, classifying, packaging and blending equipment can be difficult to vent adequately. Such equipment should be located in an isolated

cubicle, itself vented to a safe place. Personnel should not be able to enter this cubicle while the equipment is operating (see Section 7.7 on page 185).

6.9   INTERCONNECTED VESSELS

If two vessels are connected together by a pipe, a dust explosion ignited in a vessel (Vessel 1) will be communicated to the second vessel (Vessel 2) and steps should be taken to isolate it.

In the second vessel the flame from the interconnecting pipe will act as a jet ignition source; there will be increased turbulence and possibly some precompression of the dust cloud. These effects can be expected to enhance the rate of pressure rise in the second vessel. Experiments in a pneumatic conveying system has shown the effect that flame jet injection can have on reduced explosion pressures in a cyclone[59].

Experiments in interconnected vessels have demonstrated that enhanced explosion effects are not necessarily limited to the second vessel. There are circumstances where increased explosion pressures can be generated in both vessels.

Two effects are apparent: firstly, the more rigorous conditions under which the explosion takes place in Vessel 2, remote from the primary ignition, and secondly, the transmission of pressure from the explosion in Vessel 2 back into Vessel 1. This latter effect results in a double peak structure to the pressure-time trace measured in Vessel 1. The first peak is due to the explosion of the dust cloud in Vessel 1 after primary ignition and the second peak is due to the transmission of explosion pressure from Vessel 2. In some circumstances the second peak can be higher than the first.

The relative importance of these effects depends on the degree of interconnectedness of the vessels. Short pipes of relatively large diameter give a good connection, and pressures can be expected to be enhanced in both vessels, especially if the vessel volumes are low and the volume of the pipe is comparable with the vessel volume. Long narrow pipes will result in enhanced pressures only in Vessel 2 because the pressure feedback to Vessel 1 is limited and the second peak of the double peak structure will not exceed the first peak.

At the moment only qualitative guidance is available for interconnected vessels. The nomograph approach for vent sizing can be applied to Vessel 1 if the degree of interconnectedness of the vessels can be shown to be low and there is no possibility of primary ignition in Vessel 2, ie it is always certain where primary ignition will occur. If this is not so, both vessels should be fitted with increased vent areas. When the degree of interconnectedness is high, both vessels will require vent areas much increased compared to the nomograph approach. The AFNOR nomograph described in Section 5.2.3 (page 101) may

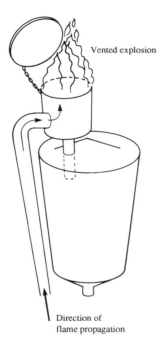

Vented explosion

Direction of
flame propagation

Figure 6.30 Explosion relief diverter.

go some way towards estimating the vent areas in these circumstances, but the difficulties associated with this method should be noted.

Venting of interconnecting ductwork is an option for decreasing the reduced explosion pressure and NFPA 68 suggests, for St 3 dusts, that a vent with an area equal to the cross-sectional area of the duct be located no more than 2 duct diameters from the connection with the vessel[16].

Alternatively, an explosion relief diverter can be fitted in the interconnecting pipeline. By this means the explosion travelling along the connecting duct is vented and the pressure released. A less violent explosion then travels into the second vessel. A diagram of a relief diverter is shown in Figure 6.30.

As an isolation device, the diverter cannot be relied upon as a flame barrier. Experiments have shown that an explosion transmission frequency can be 50–100%[59]. Similarly, although explosion pressures can be reduced this is not always the case.

Quantitative guidance for venting of interconnected vessels is not available. A research project is currently under way, the results of which will provide such guidance.

If the vessels are isolated by fast acting valves or extinguisher barriers controlled by explosion detection systems then each vessel should be vented separately by the appropriate method. Generally if a vessel is vented then any vessel communicating with it should also be protected.

It is clear from experiments in vented dust collectors[56], that explosions in collectors can flash back down the dust feed lines. It is not sufficient to hope that the velocity of the material flow into a piece of plant will be sufficient to prevent passage of the explosion. In most circumstances, it will not, and this needs to be assessed for each individual situation.

7. DESIGN OF VENT CLOSURES AND VENT DUCTING, AND SAFE DISCHARGE AREAS

The calculations of vent area make no distinction between circular or rectangular vent openings. Generally, the effects of vent shape will not be great, and there is probably enough of a safety factor to make any deviations due to vent shape unimportant. The location of the vent is important, however. It should be such that the flame front is unimpeded in its movement from ignition source towards the vent, and the passage to the vent should never be such that the flame is constrained to an area less than the area of the vent. The required vent area can be made up of a number of smaller vents provided the total area is adequate and the vent opening pressures are suitable.

Furthermore, the cloud of unburnt dust and combustion products which is ejected from an explosion vent must discharge to a safe place. This too will determine the vent location, depending on the location of other equipment, occupied areas and proximity to an outside wall.

Explosion vents must not be used as inspection hatches or access ports unless the plant is shut down. The use of vents in this way must not result in their main function — venting an explosion — to be impaired. Other ports or hatches must be securely closed and must not open in the event of an explosion.

7.1 METHODS OF VENT CLOSURE

Several types of vent closure are available. All vent closures should open at as low a pressure as is possible in the prevailing circumstances and present a minimal amount of resistance to the venting process.

A major difficulty in selecting a suitable closure is that often the difference between normal operating pressures in the process and the required opening pressure of the vent is relatively small. All vent closures need to be well maintained. There should be no rise in the opening pressure either because of build-up of process material on the inside or outside, especially when a vent duct is fitted, because of deposits of snow and ice on the outside. Likewise there must be no fall in the opening pressure because of corrosion, fatigue or other deterioration of the closure.

7.1.1 DIAPHRAGMS

A sheet or membrane of material firmly clamped around its edges can make an inexpensive vent closure. When installed correctly diaphragms are dust-tight. A wide mesh support is often fitted inside the vent when either the process is operating at pressures below atmospheric or as protection against gusts of wind or a person falling through it. The vent area must be calculated with the blockage caused by this support taken into account. A minimum spacing of 150 mm is recommended.

The membrane can be made out of a number of materials all with advantages or disadvantages. Membranes have low weight per unit area (kg/m^2) and there is little influence on the venting process. Ideally the material should tear and fragment rather than stretch before bursting, and it is important that the bursting pressure should be within ± 50% of P_{stat}. If the bursting pressure is less than four times the process operating pressure (bar g), the membrane material should be carefully selected, to avoid spurious rupture.

Bursting pressures are best measured using the size of the panel that will be used in practice because the static bursting pressure, P_{stat}, of most materials increases substantially as the area falls (< 0.15 m diameter). With some materials the dynamic bursting pressure may be markedly higher than the static bursting pressure, again especially at low areas (< 0.25 m diameter). Note, too, that variations of thickness, imperfections, moisture content and temperature can significantly affect the bursting pressure of apparently similar materials, as can the method of clamping the material, ageing and exposure to sunlight or process materials. Some materials will soften at elevated temperatures and some will become brittle in cold weather. Vibration can cause a reduction in the diaphragm's working life, especially if the area is large. Regular inspection is recommended and regular replacement of diaphragms may be necessary. A selection of readily-available materials for use as bursting panels is listed in Table 7.1 on pages 158–159.

Table 7.2 on pages 160–161 provides an approximate guide to the static bursting pressure of a number of common materials. This information is no substitute for testing of the actual material. As a first approximation, the bursting pressure of membranes which burst in tension is proportional to (thickness)/(linear dimension). For rigid panels such as insulating boards, the breaking pressure is inversely proportional to the area. When vent areas are large it is good practice to break up the vent into smaller vents with the same total area, but maintain the same opening pressure. It is advisable to test for the dynamic bursting pressure as well as the static. Although some methods for estimating venting requirements use the static opening pressure, for design purposes the maximum vent opening pressure — static or dynamic — should be used.

An example of a membrane vent closure is shown in Figure 7.1 on page 162.

Many diaphragm materials are electrically insulating and there is the possibility of a static charge build-up. The subsequent build-up of dust on the

TABLE 7.1
Materials for non-proprietary bursting panels

Material	Special properties
(1) Kraft paper.	Tears easily, therefore effective as a vent, but rather delicate. Unsuitable in wet conditions.
(2) Waxed paper.	As (1), but resists moisture.
(3) Paper/aluminium laminate.	
(4) Plastic-impregnated paper.	Resists moisture but may not tear as easily as (1).
(5) Plastic-impregnated cloth.	
(6) Rubberized compressed fibre (eg, 'Klingerite').	Good, uniform, general purpose material. Tears easily but affected by wet. Resin varnish spraying improves waterproof properties without significantly affecting strength.
(7) 'Klingerite' faced with self-adhesive aluminium foil on both sides.	More waterproof and weather resistant than ordinary 'Klingerite'.
(8) Plastic films: (a) Polyethylene film	At low rates of pressure rise, tends to balloon and does not burst quickly. A knife point is therefore recommended. May not give full opening as it does not tear easily. Withstands pressure fluctuations well.
(b) Polypropylene film ('Propafilm')	Similar to (8)(a) but stronger.
(c) Polyester film ('Melinex')	Much stronger than polyethylene but a more precise bursting pressure as made to an exacting specification.

TABLE 7.1 (continued)
Materials for non-proprietary bursting panels

Material	Special properties
(d) PTFE sheet	Not as readily available in thin sheets as (8)(a), (b) and (c). More expensive than above films. Nevertheless, often used and is a standard material from bursting disc manufacturers.
(e) Polyethylene film/aluminium foil sandwich	Thought to be more reliable than plain polyethylene film.
(f) Cellophane.	Delicate material, tears easily.
(9) Aluminium foil.	Subject to fatigue problems.
(10) Thick, rigid sheets of polystyrene foam.	Brittle type of failure, different from the others above and more often installed as a pop-out panel mounting.
(11) Lightweight insulating board, faced both sides with 'Klingerite'.	Very suitable for large panels on weak plant.
(12) 50 mm Rockwool, each side faced with 0.2 mm 'Klingerite'.	Suitable for dryer backs.

diaphragm may cause the bursting characteristics to change. If available, electrically conducting diaphragm materials are preferable to insulating ones, although they must be used with conducting gasket material or otherwise connected to earth.

Thin diaphragms provide no thermal insulation over the vent area. If thermal insulation is needed rockwool faced on either side of a membrane has proved effective.

7.1.2 BURSTING PANELS

Proprietary bursting panels are designed to open at pre-set values of P_{stat}. Usually they comprise scored metal sheets either backed by or sandwiching a PTFE membrane. When the panel opens the sectors petal apart, practically without

TABLE 7.2
Example of the static bursting pressure of materials

	Approximate bursting pressure, bar g				
Panel area	0.03 m^2	0.1 m^2	0.3 m^2	1.0 m^2	3.0 m^2
Material					
Paper: 0.12 mm thick.			0.03 at 0.22 m^2		
(CAF) 'Klingerite': 0.2 mm.	0.55	0.3	0.07		
'Klingerite': 0.2 mm faced with aluminium foil — 40 micron each side.				0.12–0.18	
Polyethylene film:					
0.25 mm	0.52	0.31	0.17	0.09	0.05
0.10 mm	0.34	0.21	0.12	0.06	0.03
0.065 mm	0.24	0.12	0.06	0.03	0.014
0.05 mm	0.14	0.08	0.05	0.02	0.01
Polyester film: 0.023 mm.			0.22 at 0.24 m^2		
PTFE sheet: 0.5 mm.			0.58 max		
Cellophane: 0.04 mm.		0.07 at 0.17 m^2			

160

TABLE 7.2 (continued)
Example of the static bursting pressure of materials

Panel area	Approximate bursting pressure, bar g				
	$0.03 \, m^2$	$0.1 \, m^2$	$0.3 \, m^2$	$1.0 \, m^2$	$3.0 \, m^2$
Material					
Soft aluminium foil:					
0.05 mm			0.14		
0.04 mm	0.03	0.18	0.10	0.06	0.03
0.025 mm	0.17 to 0.24	0.09 to 0.12	0.05 to 0.06	0.02 to 0.03	0.01 to 0.014
Aluminium (hard):					
0.25 mm.	1.70	0.76	0.41	0.19	0.10
Expanded polystyrene:					
8.0 mm.		0.03	Almost nil		
50 mm Rockwool faced each side with 0.2 mm 'Klingerite'.				0.015 bar g at $0.8 \, m^2$	

inertia, leaving an unobstructed vent. The panel can not close once the explosion is over and because of this any fires following from the explosion will not be extinguished. When the explosion is particularly violent, metal sectors can tear completely away and be projected for several metres. These panels usually operate within 10% of the quoted P_{stat}, although an elevated temperature will alter the opening pressure. Vibration or flutter of panels can cause a reduction in the working life of bursting panels especially if the area is large and P_{stat} is low.

Figure 7.1   Membrane vent closure on dust filter/collector.

Proprietary bursting panels are preferred when the operating pressure is between 25% and 70% of the required vent opening pressure and when premature failure cannot be permitted. The metal cover on these vents renders them impervious to severe weather, although deposits of snow and ice will increase the opening pressure.

The minimum opening pressure of these vent closures is 0.07 bar g, although at low vent areas (< 0.6 m dia) the minimum will be higher. A bursting disc is shown in Figure 7.2.

Other designs of bursting disc using domed and flat metal and composites are available, as are brittle graphite discs. One design is a closure of special glass which is ruptured by a small detonator embedded in it. A sensor detects the explosion in its early stages, and triggers the detonator with an electrical signal. Full details of proprietary bursting panels or discs are available from the manufacturers; the IChemE Library and Information Service will be able to assist in locating manufacturers.

Figure 7.2   Example of a bursting disc.

7.1.3   RIGID PANELS

When the panel is held in place by a method that is less strong than the material of the panel, the panel will be ejected bodily from the vent opening when the explosion occurs; these vent closures are known as rigid panels or 'pop-out' panels. The panels must have low weight (kg/m²) and should be easily swept aside by the blast of the explosion so that there is minimal obstruction to the flow. Hinged or even loose panels can also be used. Panels can be arranged vertically or horizontally, or at an angle in between. For negative pressure systems the weight of a horizontal plate might provide a suitable seal. Panels can operate at low overpressures (0.06 to 0.1 bar g) and generally have high stability, although very large panels should not be installed on vertical surfaces unless they have the necessary rigidity. The relief pressure of a 'pop-out' panel must be set with fairly wide tolerances; it will depend on thickness of the panel, area of clamping, the force of the clamping, the dimension and shape, the sheet and its material.

Loose explosion panels can be kept in place and sealed by a variety of methods, and it is usual to provide a tight seal between panel and vessel. Greased felt or foam rubber as shown in Figure 7.3 (see page 164) has been recommended by the HSE[60], while a closed cell sponge neoprene rubber with a density of 200–300 kg/m³ has been found particularly suitable[61]. Foam rubber gaskets need some compression to give a satisfactory seal, and although in horizontal positions the weight of the panel may be sufficient, some further loading by means of latches or spring-loaded catches — but not by the addition of loose weights — may be necessary. The force exerted by this increased retention of the panel must be taken into account when estimating vent areas.

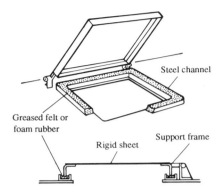

Figure 7.3   Felt or foam panel seal.

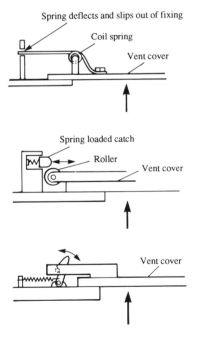

Figure 7.4   Spring catches.

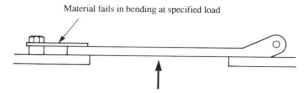

Material fails in bending at specified load

Figure 7.5   Bending clip.

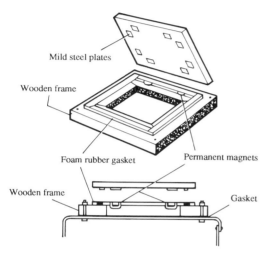

Mild steel plates

Wooden frame

Foam rubber gasket   Permanent magnets

Wooden frame   Gasket

Figure 7.6   Magnet catch.

One popular method of securing metal panels is by shaped rubber clamps around the entire periphery. Rubber clamps need regular inspection so that any corrosion does not go unnoticed.

Spring-loaded latches, clips which fail by bending, shear pins, pull-through washers and 'pop'-rivets can be used to retain panels, but care must be taken to ensure the catches fail at the proper pressure — reliance should not be placed on manufacturer's values — and that corrosion, lack of lubrication and snow and ice have not rendered them ineffective. Dynamic testing is necessary to establish opening pressures. Figures 7.4 and 7.5 demonstrate spring catches and a bending clip respectively.

Permanent magnets can be used to secure horizontally fixed vent panels[60]. The magnets are fixed to the vessel so as not to increase the weight of the panel. The relief pressure must be determined by test. The principle is shown in Figure 7.6.

Figure 7.7   Blow-out panel.

Panels should be restrained by wire ropes or chains to prevent them acting as missiles. The chains should be equal to the length of the longest side of the panel, and restraints need to be carefully designed and tested for the type of application. If a vent duct is in place a cage can be fitted over the end to catch the panel without causing any subsequent impediment to flow, ie extending at least one duct diameter out from the end. The design of duct should be such as to prevent the panel jamming inside the duct and so restricting the gas flow. A typical design of panel is shown in Figure 7.7.

7.1.4   HINGED PANELS AND EXPLOSION DOORS

Hinged doors and panels flip open in the event of an explosion and in principle this makes little difference to the vent as once the door has opened to 45° there is little restriction to free venting. Doors should be sufficiently strong that they are not destroyed or deformed, but their weight should be appropriate to the strength of the enclosure that they are designed to protect. Low strength doors should not be fitted to high strength equipment and likewise high strength doors should not be fitted to low strength equipment. Compared to panels and diaphragms of the same area, the efficiency of explosion doors is only about 80% for low weight doors, and 60% for high weight doors, and this needs to be taken into account when calculating the vent area.

The venting efficiency of an explosion door is defined by the equation:

$$\text{Venting efficiency} = \frac{A_1 \times 100}{A_2}\ \%$$

where A_1 is the vent area necessary to produce a given value of the reduced explosion pressure, P_{red}, when a bursting disc is used, and A_2 is the vent area necessary to produce the same value of P_{red} when an explosion door is fitted.

Hinged doors and panels can close once the explosion has vented. The ingress of air to support fires that might follow the explosion is thus prevented. However, cooling of the hot combustion gases inside the vessel may result in a sub-atmospheric internal pressure which could damage weak equipment, although usually there are other inlets through which air can enter.

Explosion door hinges can become stiff with lack of maintenance and the doors will then not respond as quickly as expected. Hinges should have large clearances to avoid seizure and they and the mountings should be strong enough to carry the maximum explosion load. The maximum force on the hinges can in some circumstances exceed the weight of the door seventy fold[7]. Because the dynamic force on the door can be very large a stop bar at the radius of gyration of the door or shock absorbing buffer springs can be provided.

Very strong explosion doors should be used for the end-venting of pipelines if high pressure deflagrations or detonations are to be vented, so that damage to the doors should not occur. An explosion door is shown in Figure 7.8.

Figure 7.8   Explosion door (720 × 370 mm) with resilient buffer.

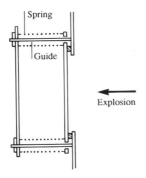

Figure 7.9   Spring loaded vent cover (schematic).

7.1.5   SPRING-LOADED VENT COVERS
Another form of self-closing cover or door uses springs. The relief pressure is determined by the weight of the cover and the characteristics of the springs. Spring systems are less widely used than other closures, probably because of cost, complexity and need for more careful maintenance. A diagram of the principle is given in Figure 7.9.

7.2   DYNAMICS OF VENT OPENING
Vents should open to their fullest extent as rapidly as possible after the initial rupture. Experiments show that proprietary bursting panels can go from initial opening to fully open in less than 20 ms. Experiments with propane explosions show[62] that the opening time increases linearly with the vent panel inertia (kg/m^2). The maximum explosion pressure occurred before the vent was fully open in these experiments. Experiments using vertical explosion doors in a duct[63], and with an inertia of approximately 40 kg/m^2 showed that the maximum explosion pressure occurred 170 ms–230 ms after the door began to open and when the angle of opening was 20°–40°. The flame continued to expand along the duct and the door was fully open within 360 ms–410 ms. Restricting to 45° the angle to which the door could open caused no difference to the maximum explosion pressure.

Other experiments[64, 65] also show that the reduced explosion pressure P_{red} increases linearly with vent closure inertia, both for doors and bursting panels. The rate of increase, mbar/(kg/m^2), depends on the conditions.

7.3   INSTALLATION AND MAINTENANCE OF VENT COVERS

Correctly designed vent closures will only operate satisfactorily and thus guarantee safety if they are installed properly and maintained to a high standard. Important factors that must be considered are listed below.

• Access to the vent by personnel should be prevented, while the plant is operating.

• Vent covers should be clearly identified as such.

• Vents should not be used as inspection or access ports, whilst the plant is operating.

• Vent covers should never be fixed closed or covered whilst the plant is operating.

• Inspection and maintenance of vents should not be carried out whilst the process is operating.

• When necessary snow should be removed from vent covers.

• Icing around seals and hinges should be expected in some circumstances and it may be necessary to provide trace heating.

• The condition of vent closures should be checked frequently and replaced as necessary. In some circumstances routine replacement may be more appropriate.

• Check freedom of hinges; clean and lubricate as appropriate.

• Check latches and spring clips.

• Check for corrosion around panels and doors.

• Check condition of gaskets and seals.

• Check for dust build-up on the inside of vents, and outside if a vent duct is fitted.

• Check integrity of panel restraints.

• Remove debris from covers and ducts.

7.4   THE EFFECT OF VENT DUCTS

In practice, venting is not simply a matter of allowing the dust cloud and flame to disperse anywhere. Dust clouds ejected from a vented explosion can be large, and the resulting external fireball is an obvious danger to personnel and equipment. Venting to a safe place is very important and will have implications for plant layout and access. If the dust-handling equipment cannot be placed in the open air, then it is best practice to guide the burning cloud to a safe place through a vent duct fitted to the vent opening. Generally, upward facing vents or vent duct outlets passing through the roof of a factory will be safe provided access to that part of the roof is strictly limited to those occasions when the plant is not operating. Vents from the side of equipment located on a factory roof should be safe provided surrounding buildings and other roof mounted equipment are far enough away.

Vents from the side of a factory or from equipment located outside a factory building should not be directed towards other equipment or towards any thoroughfare, either traffic or pedestrian, and access to the vicinity of the vent must be prevented during plant operation.

Vents should not discharge into the factory or any other building containing plant or where personnel may be present. Flame and overpressure hazards are always a danger, and personnel must be totally excluded from any enclosed space into which plant is vented during operation of the plant. If there is no option but to vent inside a building, account must also be taken of the rise in pressure inside the building or room and its effect on the structure. The avoidance of secondary explosions by good housekeeping and regular cleaning is of particular importance.

In the final analysis, however, the requirement to vent to a safe place may sometimes be impossible to achieve without very expensive plant modifications. In such circumstances venting is unsuitable and alternative measures should be used (see Chapter 2).

The fitting of a vent duct complicates the venting requirements. Its presence alters the outflow characteristics of the vent, and whereas the venting requirements may have been appropriate for a vessel standing on its own, once a duct is fitted the reduced explosion pressure may be increased to a point at which it exceeds the strength of the vessel.

7.4.1   CALCULATING THE EFFECT OF A VENT DUCT ON THE REDUCED EXPLOSION PRESSURE

The increases in the reduced explosion pressure that can be expected are shown in Figures 7.10 and 7.11[66] (see pages 171 and 172). All the graphs demonstrate an increase in the reduced explosion pressure measured in the explosion vessel as the length to diameter (L/D) ratio of the vent duct increases, although at low L/D ratios the reduced explosion pressure falls slightly relative to the value when no vent duct is present.

Guidance for the design of vent ducts is published by the IChemE[14], giving information on the effect of vent ducts on the reduced explosion pressures.

Figure 7.12 on page 173 gives some examples of this guidance, which has been designed to engage with the K_{st} nomographs described in Chapter 4.

The complete guidance consists of three sets of such graphs; one set is applicable to straight vent ducts, one to ducts containing one sharp 45° bend and one to ducts containing a sharp 90° bend. Each set contains a graph for each

Vessel volume: 18.5 m³
(A) Coal dust. Vent diam: 1.1 m, area: 0.95 m², P_{stat}: 1.2 bar a, duct: 45° bend.
(B) Coal dust. Vent diam: 1.1 m, area: 0.95 m², P_{stat}: 1.2 bar a, duct: 90° bend.
(C) Aspirin dust. Vent diam: 1.1 m, area: 0.95 m², open vent, duct: 45° bend.

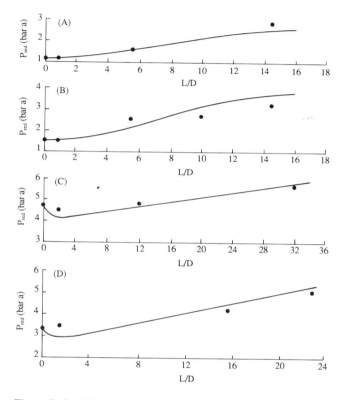

Figure 7.10 Effect of vent duct on reduced explosion pressure.

combination of K_{st} value and P_{stat} that is represented on the K_{st} nomographs (Chapter 4). The graphs are applicable to dusts with P_{max} values to 11 bar a for groups St 1 and St 2 dusts and 13 bar a for group St 3 dusts.

The ordinate of each graph represents $(P_{red})_0$, the reduced explosion pressure when no vent duct is fitted. For known vessel volume, dust K_{st} value, vent bursting pressure and vent area, $(P_{red})_0$ is estimated by using the K_{st} nomographs. When a vent duct is fitted to the vent the new reduced explosion pressure, P_{red}, is found at any value of L/D ratio by moving along the abscissa to the correct value and then reading P_{red} from the appropriate line.

Vessel volume: 18.5 m³ straight duct
(A) Coal dust. Vent diam: 1.1 m, area: 0.95 m², P_{stat}: 1.2 bar a.
(B) Aspirin dust. Vent diam: 1.1 m, area: 0.95 m², open vent.
(C) Coal dust. Vent diam: 1.1 m, area: 0.195 m², P_{stat}: 1.5 bar a.
(D) Aspirin dust. Vent diam: 0.7 m, area: 0.385 m², P_{stat}: 1.1 bar a.

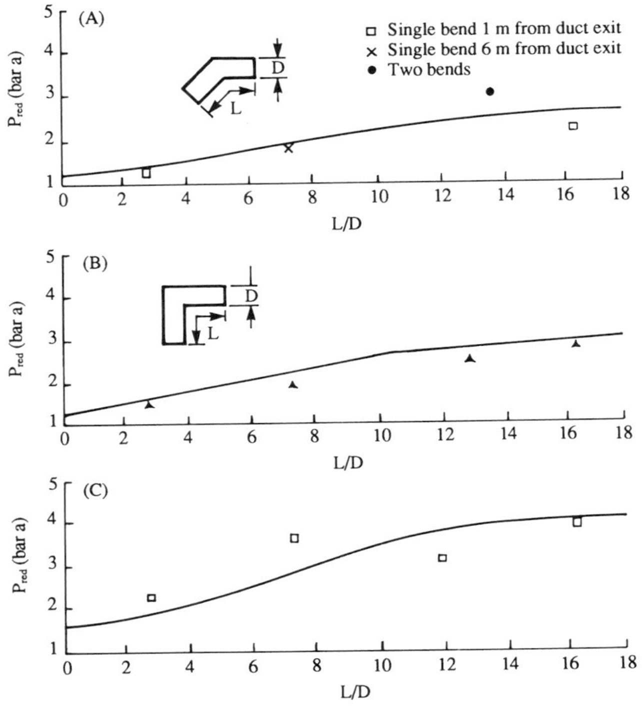

Figure 7.11   Effect of vent duct on reduced explosion pressure.

The guidance establishes two simple principles:

(1) All other things remaining equal, as the volume of the vented vessel increases the volume of the vent duct must increase pro rata if the same reduced explosion is to be obtained. The current VDI vent duct guidance does not include this effect because it uses duct length L as the characterizing parameter rather than the L/D ratio.

(2) In any particular situation, when the allowable $(P_{red})_o$ increases, the vent area decreases, and so does the vent diameter. For a given vent duct L/D ratio the duct length thus decreases also. Thus, as the allowable $(P_{red})_o$ increases, the

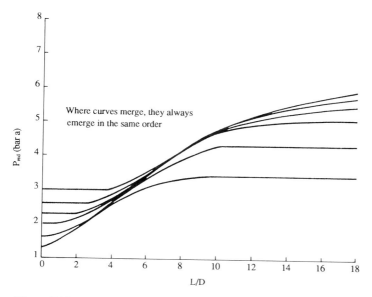

Figure 7.12 Example of guidance on effect of vent ducts.

volume of the vent duct decreases relative to the volume of the vessel and the effect on the reduced explosion pressure at a given *L/D* ratio is in some circumstances correspondingly less.

Methods for using the new vent duct guidance are demonstrated in some worked examples. The following qualifications should be noted when the guidance is used:

- The length of the duct should not exceed 16 m. The *L/D* ratio of the duct should not exceed a value of 18.

- Any bend should be incorporated as far from the vent opening as possible and at least 2 m from the vent opening.

- Multiple bends are not recommended.

- If the open end of the vent duct is protected by a mesh, the mesh should present the minimum possible obstruction to the flow.

- The vent duct must be capable of withstanding the explosion pressures generated inside the explosion vessel.

- Reaction forces from the vented explosion must be considered not only for the vented vessel but in some cases for the duct as well.

The IChemE guidance demonstrates both volume and K_{st} value dependency.

173

The vent duct guidance published by the IChemE has been designed to be used with the original K_{st} nomographs. It can be used when vent area predictions are made using alternative methods that reduce the vent area for a given reduced explosion pressure, $(P_{red})_o$, eg the Radandt nomographs for dusts with low values of P_{max} (see Chapter 5) and the guidance applicable to pneumatic filling (see Chapter 6). It should not be used with methods that lead to increased vent areas, eg the AFNOR nomographs for high turbulence situations (Chapter 5).

The results when these alternative methods are used will not be as precise as with the K_{st} nomographs, but they will be conservative.

The recommended procedure is to use the guidance in the usual way, but to calculate the L/D ratio used with the guidance by the equation:

$$\left(\frac{L}{D}\right)_{guidance} = \left(\frac{L}{D_2}\right)\left(\frac{D_1}{D_2}\right)$$

Where $(L/D)_{guidance}$ is the ratio to be used when applying the guidance, (L/D_2) is the ratio of the actual vent duct length to the diameter of the vent calculated by the original K_{st} nomograph approach for the given value of $(P_{red})_o$, and D_1 is the diameter of the vent calculated by the alternative vent sizing approach for the same $(P_{red})_o$.

This procedure equalizes the volume of the vent duct used for the purpose of the guidance and the actual volume of the vent duct. Using the guidance with the actual vent duct L/D ratio would overestimate the addition to $(P_{red})_o$ due to the presence of the duct.

This procedure does not take into account the reduced rate of combustion in the explosion within the duct that is a result of either the lower P_{max} of the dust or the lower turbulence of the dust cloud. A lower rate of combustion will tend to reduce the effect of the vent duct on the reduced explosion pressure inside the vessel.

7.4.2   VENT DUCTS WITH ENHANCED AREA

Under some circumstances, the use of a vent duct with a cross-sectional area greater than the area of vent opening can result in lower reduced explosion pressures than if the duct and opening had equal areas. Measurements suggest[67] that the effect is limited to circumstances in which the reduced explosion pressure in an unducted vented explosion, $(P_{red})_o$, does not exceed 0.5 bar g and where the duct area to vent area ratio does not exceed 2. Values of P_{stat} should not exceed 0.1 bar g. Nevertheless, this technique is not recommended unless it has been validated for a particular situation. In some circumstances high reduced explosion pressures can be generated if the duct area is greater than the vent area.

7.5   WORKED EXAMPLES

7.5.1   ESTIMATING THE REDUCED EXPLOSION PRESSURE WHEN A VENT DUCT OF KNOWN L/D RATIO IS FITTED

This example demonstrates the simple, straightforward way of using the guidance to estimate the reduced explosion pressure that a vented vessel with a known vent area will need to withstand when a vent duct is fitted.

EXAMPLE 5

A dust collector of 6 m^3 capacity is used to handle a dust with a K_{st} value of 150 bar m s^{-1}. A vent with an area of 0.7 m^2 is fitted, closed with a vent panel having an opening pressure, P_{stat}, of 1.2 bar a. A vent duct 5 m long containing a 45° bend is to be attached to the vent opening. Estimate the reduced explosion pressure in the collector.

(a) Use the K_{st} nomograph to find the reduced explosion pressure before the vent duct is fitted, $(P_{red})_0$.

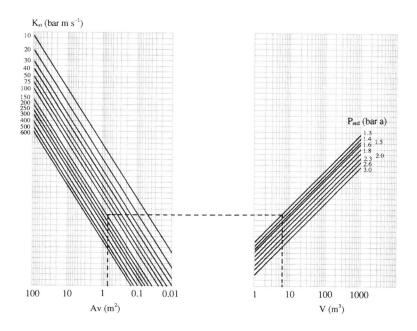

$(P_{red})_0 = 1.31$ bar a

Take 5 m to be the length of the duct, L, as measured by the method shown in Figure 16.

The diameter of the duct, D, $= (4 \times 0.7/3.142)^{1/2} = 0.944$m

L/D ratio $= 5/0.944 = 5.3$

From the vent duct guidance for $K_{st} = 150$ bar m s^{-1}, $P_{stat} = 1.2$ bar a and vent duct containing a sharp 45° bend:

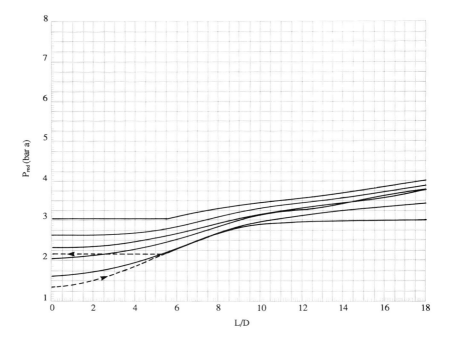

When $(P_{red})_0 = 1.31$ bar a and vent duct L/D ratio $= 5.3$, the reduced explosion pressure $= 2.1$ bar a.

ANSWER: Reduced explosion pressure $= 2.1$ bar a.

7.5.2   USING THE VENT DUCT GUIDANCE WITH VENT AREA PREDICTION METHODS OTHER THAN THE K_{st} NOMOGRAPHS

This example demonstrates the method required for using the vent duct guidance with the Radandt nomographs for compact enclosures and dusts with maximum explosion pressures, P_{max}, less than 10 bar a.

EXAMPLE 6

A dust collector of 20 m³ capacity handles an St 1 dust. A vent of area 0.9 m² is fitted, and the vent panel has a static bursting pressure of 1.1 bar a (0.1 bar g). A straight vent duct 6 m long is to be attached. Estimate the reduced explosion pressure in the collector assuming the dust has a maximum explosion pressure of 10 bar a (9 bar g).

A_1, the actual vent area, $= 0.9$ m², and D_1, the actual vent diameter, $= 1.07$ m. The reduced explosion pressure when no vent duct is fitted, $(P_{red})_0$, is obtained from the Radandt nomograph:

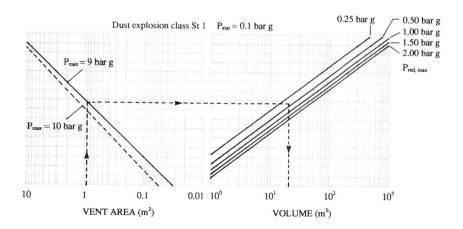

Following the dotted line, $(P_{red})_0 = 1.38$ bar a (0.38 bar g). The least troublesome method would be to next use the vent duct guidance with an L/D ratio calculated from the actual duct length and the actual vent diameter, ie,

$$\frac{L}{D_1} = 6/1.07 = 5.6$$

177

But the addition to $(P_{red})_0$ then calculated as resulting from the vent duct would be excessive because the volume of duct assumed by the calculation is larger than that of the real duct.

To make a more realistic estimate of the pressure increase, the volume of the duct used with the vent duct guidance needs to be reduced so that it equals the volume of the real duct. This can be done in two stages. Firstly, estimate the vent area from the original K_{st} or St nomographs which would give the same $(P_{red})_0$ as before, ie 1.38 bar a (0.38 bar g) in this example.

From the appropriate graph, in this case an St nomograph:

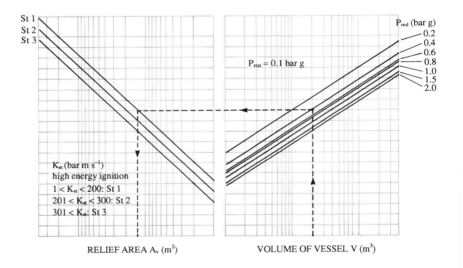

RELIEF AREA A_v (m^2)   VOLUME OF VESSEL V (m^3)

The vent area $A_2 = 1.3$ m^2 and the diameter $D_2 = 1.29$ m.

Secondly, calculate the L/D ratio to use with the guidance. This is done using the simple equation:

$$\left(\frac{L}{D}\right)_{GUIDANCE} = \left(\frac{L}{D_2}\right)\left(\frac{D_1}{D_2}\right)$$

where $(L/D)_{GUIDANCE}$ is the ratio for use with the guidance.

178

Thus, for this example,

$$\left(\frac{L}{D}\right)_{\text{GUIDANCE}} = \left(\frac{6.0}{1.29}\right)\left(\frac{1.07}{1.29}\right) = 3.86$$

This procedure equalizes the volume of the duct assumed by the vent duct guidance and the real vent duct volume.

Using the appropriate graph from the vent duct guidance for $P_{\text{stat}} = 1.1$ bar a (0.1 bar g), $K_{\text{st}} = 200$ bar m s^{-1} and a straight vent duct:

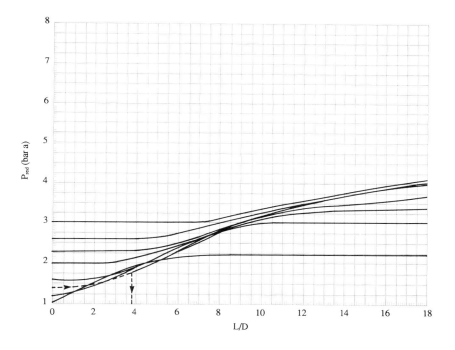

The reduced explosion pressure $P_{\text{red}} = 1.80$ bar a (0.80 bar g). (If the actual duct L/D ratio has been used, the P_{red} would have been 2.2 bar a.)

7.5.3 DETERMINE THE VENT AREA NECESSARY TO LIMIT THE REDUCED EXPLOSION PRESSURE TO A GIVEN VALUE WHEN THE LENGTH OF THE VENT DUCT IS FIXED AT A KNOWN VALUE

When a vessel is to be explosion vented and the allowable reduced explosion pressure is fixed, an estimate of the vent area must take the effects of the vent duct into account.

179

EXAMPLE 7

An item of equipment having a free volume of 16 m³ is being used with a dust of K_{st} value 250 bar m s^{-1}. The opening pressure of the vent, P_{stat}, is 1.5 bar a. The vent area is 1.3 m², sufficient to limit the reduced explosion pressure to 1.5 bar a, according to the K_{st} nomographs. If a straight vent duct 6.14 m in length is attached to the vent opening, calculate the new reduced explosion pressure. Determine a vent area which, when fitted with a vent duct 6.14 m long, will return the reduced explosion pressure to 2.5 bar a.

The vent diameter, D, $= (4 \times 1.3/3.142)^{1/2} = 1.29$ m.

The vent duct L/D ratio $= 6.14/1.29 = 4.76$.

From the vent duct guidance for $K_{st} = 250$ bar m s^{-1}, $P_{stat} = 1.5$ bar a and a straight vent duct:

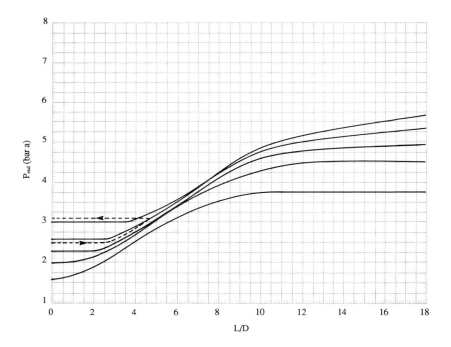

When $(P_{red})_0 = 2.5$ bar a and $L/D = 4.76$, the new reduced explosion pressure equals 3.1 bar a.

New reduced explosion pressure = 3.1 bar a.

A trial and error method is needed to answer the second part of this problem. A L/D ratio required to produce a reduced explosion pressure of 2.5 bar a is compared to the actual L/D ratio at several values of $(P_{red})_0$.

The required vent area is obtained when the two values of L/D ratio are equal.

So, using once again the vent duct guidance for $K_{st} = 250$ bar m s^{-1}, P_{stat} = 1.5 bar a and a straight duct:

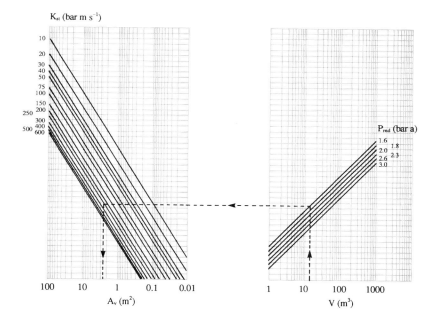

When $(P_{red})_0 = 1.6$ bar a, a vent duct with L/D ratio = 3.9 is required to give a reduced explosion pressure of 2.5 bar a.

The vent area required to give a $(P_{red})_0$ of 1.6 bar a in a 16 m^3 enclosure when $K_{st} = 250$ bar m s^{-1} and $P_{stat} = 1.5$ bar a can be estimated from the appropriate K_{st} nomograph.

At these conditions the vent area equals 2.4 m^2, with a diameter, D, = $2.4 \times 4/3.142)^{\frac{1}{2}} = 1.75$ m.

Thus the actual L/D ratio = 6.14/1.75 = 3.51, which is less than the required L/D ratio.

When $(P_{red})_0 = 1.7$ bar a, the vent duct guidance again gives a required L/D ratio:

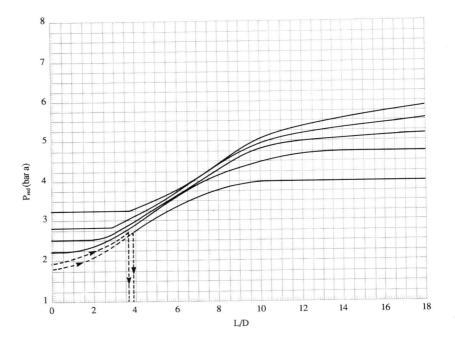

The required L/D ratio equals 3.7 for a reduced explosion pressure of 2.5 bar a.

Again using the appropriate K_{st} nomograph, the vent area to give a $(P_{red})_0 = 1.7$ bar a using a dust with $K_{st} = 250$ bar m s^{-1} in a 16 m^3 enclosure when $P_{stat} = 1.5$ bar a can be estimated:

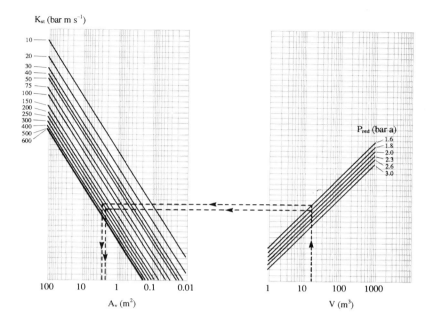

The vent area = 2.1 m^2, and the vent diameter = $(4 \times 2.1/3.142)^{1/2}$ = 1.63 m.

The actual L/D ratio = 6.14/1.63 = 3.77, which, in this case, is greater than the required L/D ratio.

A simple graphical construction is used to give the required vent area:

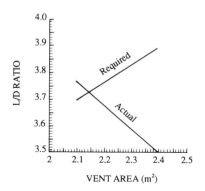

The vent area to limit the reduced explosion pressure to 2.5 bar a = 2.15 m^2.

This example has been completed by calculating the L/D ratios at two values of $(P_{red})_o$ only. It may be necessary to repeat the calculations at further values of $(P_{red})_o$, depending on the initial choice of $(P_{red})_o$, before a final answer is obtained.

When the measured K_{st} value lies between graphs, either carry out the calculation using the graph for the K_{st} value immediately above the measured value, or carry out the calculation at K_{st} values bracketing the measured value and then interpolate to estimate the vent area.

Example 7 is essentially a repeated application of a problem such as Example 6 by a trial and error method, with interpolation between the points.

7.6   THE Q-PIPE

The quench-pipe, or Q-pipe, is a device which has been recently developed and which is designed to allow venting of explosions without the attendant risks of an external fire-ball and without the use of vent ducts[68].

The principle of the Q-pipe is demonstrated in Figure 7.13. It is, essentially, a flame arrester, comprising a porous, heat absorbing surface in the form of a pipe. The vented explosion is captured in the pipe, but gases are cooled as they pass through the porous surface, and the flame is quenched. Particulate matter is retained in the pipe. The quenching surface area of the Q-pipe is

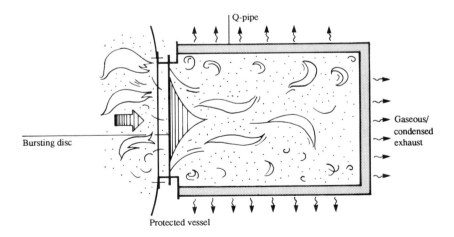

Figure 7.13 Q-pipe principle, combining filter and quenching effects without causing considerable flow resistances. (Reproduced by permission of Rembe® GmbH and Christian Michelsen Institute.)

designed so that the effective vent area is almost the same as if the vent itself was free. The proprietors of the device say that the effect on the reduced explosion pressure, P_{red}, of the vented explosion is then minimal.

Although experiments using a 5.8 m^3 bag filter have proved the effectiveness of the Q-pipe[69] at least in the small scale, its use in any particular situation should be validated. The quenching surface must be dimensioned for the volume to be protected. High dust loads in the vented explosion can cause partial blocking of the porous surface, as can the vent closure if this is, for instance, a diaphragm which can tear away from the vent opening and then blank off part of the porous area.

Various other options have been proposed for the use of the Q-pipe; an open-ended version acting as a vent duct, or a Q-pipe followed by a normal duct. Both would be expected to reduce the pressure immediately external to the vent opening. However, these options must be validated before they can be used in practice.

7.7 VENTING OF BUILDINGS CONTAINING DUST-HANDLING EQUIPMENT

In some cases it may be impossible to satisfactorily duct a vented explosion to a safe external area. If venting has to be into an enclosed area such as a room or building, there must be no risk or danger to personnel or damage to the building containing the dust-handling equipment, through either pressure or flame effects, including secondary explosions.

Although the successful venting of a dust explosion may eliminate high overpressures inside the plant, the effects of the vented explosion outside the vent cannot be discounted. The most obvious effect is that a flame is ejected; but because dust explosions inside plant usually involve more dust than can be burnt by the available oxygen if the explosion is confined, much unburnt dust is also ejected from the vent. A secondary flash explosion can then take place ignited by the vented flame and utilizing the oxygen from the surrounding air.

The blast and pressure effects from the vented explosion can also have harmful consequences. The pressure may be sufficient, at least, to cause damage to ear drums and the blast can result in serious injury to personnel if they are bowled over by the jet from the vent. Nearby plant may also be damaged. It cannot be stressed too often that it is best practice to site vented plant in the open air; where this is impractical the vented explosion should be ducted to a safe place free from personnel.

For some small vessels, however, explosion venting may be viable without ducting so long as the vent discharges in a safe direction and:

• Personnel are prevented entirely from gaining access to the vicinity of the vent while the plant is operating.

• Secondary explosions are under no circumstances allowed to develop. The blast from the vented explosions will disturb dust layers and dust accumulation that have collected in the work-place, dispersing it into the air to form a cloud which will fuel an explosion of much more destructive potential than the original event. These secondary explosions can be extensive and good housekeeping is necessary to ensure that dust accumulations are not allowed to build up in any location. Very thin layers of dust can cause explosible dust clouds when dispersed.

• The building in which the item of vented plant is housed must be capable of resisting local overpressures caused by the vented explosion without damage.

• The building in which the item of vented plant is housed may require the installation of its own explosion vents.

It is important that the extent of the flame produced by the vented explosion be limited. Deflectors should be installed on vents to guide the vented explosion to a safe area in the building, especially away from personnel and weak parts of the structure.

Horizontal vent discharges can cause problems especially when they are at low level because of the relatively large area that is at risk. Deflection of the hot products from a vented dust explosion can be achieved by a device as shown in Figure 7.14.

The deflector plate is shown combined with a vent duct in the figure but it can also be used without a duct. The area of the deflector should be at least twice the area of the vent and the deflector inclined at 45° to send the emission

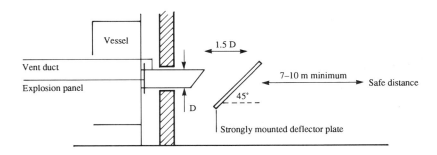

Figure 7.14 Diagram illustrating angled duct end and use of deflector plate.

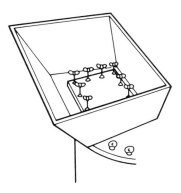

Figure 7.15   Shroud deflector. (Reprinted with permission from *Fire Protection Handbook*, 14th edition, Copyright © 1976, National Fire Protection Association, Quincy, MA 02269.)

upwards. An alternative design shrouds all sides of the vent, as shown in Figure 7.15. Care must be taken to ensure that deflection of the explosion flame does not inadvertently put other places at risk.

It may also be possible to segregate the hazardous operations into a specially constructed cubicle into which the operation may vent[60]. The door between the cubicle and the general work space should be strong, open inwards and overlap the walls so that they support the door in the event of an explosion. The door must also be interlocked with the operation to prevent access whilst the plant is operating. The walls of the cubicle inside the factory should be of suitably strong construction and vented to outdoors using the methods described herein. The outer wall of the cubicle should be constructed of a fragile material to act as an explosion relief and access to the region of the outer wall should be prohibited. Figure 7.16 on page 188 shows such a cubicle.

An alternative method may be to fit a Q-pipe external to the vent (see Section 7.5 on page 175).

Another safety application is a combined suppression-venting technique. The combination of venting the explosion and the injection of a suppressant into the flame front near to the vent opening will almost certainly reduce the safe discharge area. Injection of suppressant material into the vessel shortly after ignition will reduce the rate of pressure rise developed inside the plant, thus allowing smaller vent sizes to be fitted. Specialist help is necessary to design such systems.

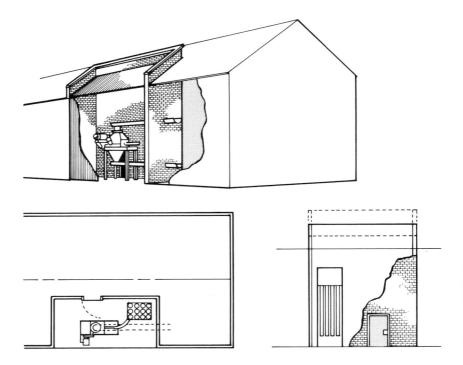

Figure 7.16   A strong cubicle designed for the grinding of particularly hazardous materials or for explosion-prone plant which cannot be situated in a safe place. (Reprinted with permission from *Fire Protection Handbook*, 14th edition, Copyright © 1976, National Fire Protection Association, Quincy, MA 02269.)

Where vessels have explosion relief opening within a building, the effect that a vented explosion can have on the building needs to be considered. Where a room is much greater in volume than the vessel in which it is situated (eg 50 times), a relieving primary explosion will cause only marginal pressure increases in the room. If the vent is close to a wall or roof panel however, significant local overpressures may result.

Where a vented vessel occupies a substantial proportion of the room volume, as in some large spray drying installations, a relieving explosion may cause a significant pressure rise in the room as a whole.

In either case the primary requirement is that a relieving explosion should not cause progressive collapse of the building by displacement of load bearing walls. A second objective should be that a venting building should cause the least risk to persons outside in the vicinity.

A method for calculating the venting requirements of buildings has been given in Chapter 5 using the equation from NFPA 68[16].

$$A_v = \frac{C_1 A_s}{(P_{red})^{1/2}}$$

where P_{red} is an overpressure and the value of C_1 is as given in Chapter 5. A_s is the total surface area (m²) including floor and ceiling, but excluding dividing walls. This equation is limited to a length to diameter ratio of 3 if a single end vent is the only arrangement possible. For non-circular buildings this restriction is:

$$L_z \leq 12\, A/p$$

where L_z is the longest dimension, A the cross-sectional area and p the perimeter of this cross-section.

7.8   WORKED EXAMPLE

EXAMPLE 8

A vessel of 250 m³ capacity is used to handle dust with a K_{st} value of 250 bar m s⁻¹. The reduced explosion pressure must not exceed 1.14 bar a (0.14 bar g). Calculate the vent area necessary to limit the reduced explosion pressure to this value and specify a value for P_{stat}, the bursting pressure of the vent cover.

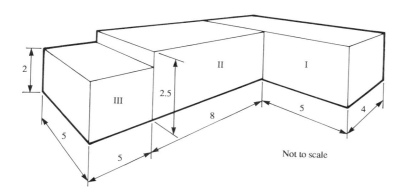

In order to demonstrate the application of this equation, the 250 m³ vessel has been divided into 3 volumes:
Volume I — 100 m³, with dimensions 2.5 × 4 × 10 m;
Volume II — 100 m³, with dimensions 2.5 × 5 × 8 m;
Volume III — 50 m³, with dimensions 2 × 5 × 5 m.
And:

Volume I — $A_s = 4 \times 2.5 \times 2 + 4 \times 10 \times 2 + 2.5 \times 10 + 2.5 \times 5 = 137.5 \text{ m}^2$;
Volume II — $A_s = 8 \times 2.5 \times 2 + 8 \times 5 \times 2 + 0.5 \times 5 = 122.5 \text{ m}^2$;
Volume III — $A_s = 5 \times 2 \times 3 + 5 \times 5 \times 2 = 80 \text{ m}^2$.

$\therefore$ Total $A_s = 340 \text{ m}^2$

For an St 2 dust, the recommended value of C_1 is 0.12 $(\text{psi})^{1/2}$.

Substituting the appropriate values into the equation gives $A_v = 0.12 \times 340/(2.06)^{1/2} = 40.8/1.43 = 28.5 \text{ m}^2$.

Vent area = 28.5 m^2.

The vent area should be distributed as equally as possible over the external surface available for venting.

Irregularly shaped buildings can be squared off to a more easily calculated shape. When parts of the wall or roof area are not available for the fitting of vents either because of fitments, presence of personnel or close proximity to other buildings, the building that is to be vented must be strengthened so that the explosion pressure that can be withstood matches the available vent area according to the equation.

However, the vent areas calculated by this equation are likely to be oversized when the dust explosion is being ejected from a vented vessel inside; it is essentially for a situation where the building has inside it a substantial dust cloud undergoing combustion. Nevertheless, the importance of good housekeeping to avoid secondary explosion cannot be overstressed. A minor explosion can quickly develop into a major event if dust is left to lie on surfaces such as window-sills, pipework and so on. A layer only one millimetre thick, when dispersed is quite capable of forming an explosible dust cloud in a building 3 m or so in height.

There remains, also, the possibility of an accidental release of large quantities of dust into the workplace through process failure, the subsequent ignition of which may cause much damage. One example of such an incident is the explosion at General Foods, Banbury[69]. The acceptability of a particular building design may be influenced by such considerations.

If buildings do not need to be totally enclosed, open vents such as louvred openings can be used, although the obstruction and decreased vent area due to the louvres must be taken into account in sizing the vent opening correctly. Otherwise the use of profiled lightweight panels attached to a steel frame is normally the preferred option for vent closures where building relief is required. The inertia of the panels should be as low as is practicable after considerations of the forces likely from wind and snow loads, but should not exceed 12 kg/m^2.

NFPA 68[16] recommends shear-type and pull through fasteners as suitable for very large vent areas such as the entire wall of a room.

Information about vent panels and appropriate fasteners is given in Section 7.1 on page 156. These panels should not be made out of brittle material which can shatter during explosion venting. Often in buildings, however, a part of the wall or roof may be designed to fail at a low overpressure. Lightweight panels are positioned between strong partition walls or may make up the entire roof. These panels must be suitably anchored to prevent wind lift. Suitable fastenings to prevent large panels acting as missiles are described in NFPA 68[16].

Windows can act as explosion vents, but shards of glass are dangerous missiles and it is best to substitute either plastic glazing or types of safety glass which will fracture into pellets. An example of a vented building is shown in Figure 7.17 and an explosion in such a building shown in Figure 7.18[70] (see page 192).

7.9 FIREBALL SIZE AND SAFE DISCHARGE AREA

The flame ejected from an explosion vent takes the form of a flame jet. The higher the reduced explosion pressure, the more jet-like the ejected flame is. Experiments in a 58 m^3 explosion vessel using dust with a K_{st} value of 130 bar m s^{-1} have shown[71] that the vent area has little influence on the flame jet length. The measured flame jet lengths were greater than 23 m under the worst conditions. Experiments in a 1 m^3 vessel gave flame jet lengths which were estimated at approximately 8 m.

Figure 7.17   Vented building. Almost 100% of the wall area of this building is explosion vent area. Each of the lightweight aluminium wall panels is secured by shear pins designed to release the panel at 30 psi. A chain at the top of each panel prevents it from being blown any distance if blown out by an explosion. (Kodak Park Industrial Photo.)

Figure 7.18 Explosion in vented building — venting an explosion of starch dust through hinged windows and hinged doors in a building of light construction.

Other experiments in vented vessels[66] have indicated that the flame jet extends approximately 18 m from a 20 m³ vessel. Other experiments in a dust collector of approximately 6 m³ capacity[56] have shown that the flame ejects to a distance of about 4 m. Vents placed well above head height are safer than vents at ground level.

It would appear that the distance the flame jet extends depends on the vessel volume. Reference 41 gives an equation for the flame length from vented cubical vessels when $P_{red} \leq 1$ bar g:

Flame length $= 8(\text{Volume})^{0.3}$

It is expected that this equation will be included in the new VDI 3673 venting guidelines.

The fitting of vent ducts does not remove the requirement to accommodate a safe discharge area. The jet of flame and dust from the exit of a vent duct can be as extensive as one from an unducted vent. Deflector plates are a useful adjunct to vented systems.

7.10   REACTION FORCES

When a vent opens and dust end combustion products are ejected, there will be a corresponding reaction force exerted on the vented vessel or duct. The mounting and support of the equipment must be sufficient to resist this reaction force if the equipment is to remain undamaged.

It is possible to calculate the theoretical value of the reaction force if the maximum pressure inside the vessel and the size of the vent opening are known, and some assumptions about the properties of the gases and the way they flow through the opening are made.

Hattwig, however, found from experiments that the theoretical maximum force was rarely approached in practice[72]. He proposed that for practical purposes the maximum reaction force be calculated from the equation:

$$R_{max} = 80A_v[(1.27(P_{red}) - 1)]$$

where R_{max} is the maximum reaction force (kN), A_v is the vent area (m^2) and P_{red}, the reduced explosion pressure, is in units of bar a.

Eckhoff has proposed a simpler relationship to estimate reaction forces when P_{red} is less than 0.5 bar g[73]:

$$R = 113A_vP_{red}$$

where R is in kN and P_{red} in bar g.

Reaction forces have implications for the siting of vents; it is best to position vents so that reaction forces are equalized if possible rather than to fit a vent to one side of a flimsy structure.

8.   EXAMPLES OF EXPLOSION VENTING IN INDUSTRIAL PLANT

This final chapter rounds off the discussion of dust explosion venting with a by no means exhaustive look at the way precautions against dust explosions are applied in real industrial plant. Even a cursory glance at the previous chapters reveals that the derivation of a basis for safety can be a complicated procedure once the configuration of the plant departs from the simplicity of a single vessel, when connections between one unit and another have to be considered and when the properties of the dust or powder have to be taken into account.

The discussions and recommendations in this chapter refer only to the examples considered. Several examples are discussed, all based on actual plant.

EXAMPLE A: SPRAY DRYER SYSTEM
The dust-handling plant is shown schematically in Figure 8.1. The plant comprises a spray drying system connected to a cyclone followed by a dust collector. The spray dryer has a length to diameter ratio of 5; it is directly fired by natural

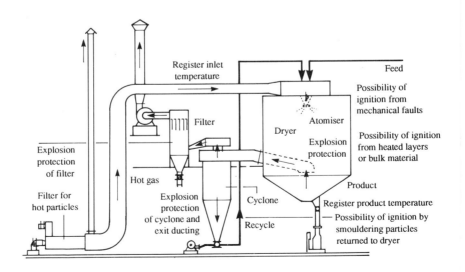

Figure 8.1   Spray dryer installation (schematic).

gas and the hot air is supplied to the dryer co-current with the spray. The spray is produced by means of a rotating disc atomizer at the top of the dryer, and dry product is collected at the base of the cyclone separator and at the base of the dust collection unit.

• Any product in the dryer should be screened for detonation or deflagrative properties (see Section 2.2 on page 20). Such materials have the properties of explosives and are not manufactured in general chemical plant; these products should be excluded.

• The dryer is not suitable for materials containing flammable solvents or which produce flammable vapour atmospheres in the dryer (hybrid mixtures — see Chapters 2 and 6).

The material assumed for this example is not an explosive, but has typical fire and explosion characteristics. It is sensitive to ignition by electrostatic discharges.

HEATING SYSTEM

• Atmospheres containing flammable gas must be prevented in the dryer system during burner ignition or if the burner malfunctions during normal operation. Flame failure protection, a pre-purge sequence, control of the gas supply and combustion air proving devices are some of the techniques and procedures used to guard against this risk.

• Hot particles from directly-fired systems can act as an ignition source of an explosible dust cloud if they enter the dryer chamber in the inlet air supply. Incandescent particles of a size less than 3–5 mm will not normally ignite a dust cloud and a mesh screen with apertures of 3 mm or less across the hot air inlet to the dryer will adequately guard against this risk. The mesh should be cleaned regularly.

• If the dryer fills with unburnt fuel gas during start-up or due to mal-operation, the burner system should be shut down and not re-started until adequate purging of the system has been performed.

SPRAY DRYER (SECTION 6.8.3 — page 148)
Various ignition sources can be identified in the dryer chamber. Exclusion of all ignition sources is not possible and explosion protection methods need to be applied since the dust is explosible as a cloud.

• The material is sensitive to ignition by static electricity discharges: all conducting plant should be earthed; non-conducting plastic material should be avoided especially in the vicinity of the product, and most especially where flammable atmospheres occur with minimum ignition energies less than 25 mJ (Section 2.1 — page 14); process personnel should be earthed by means of suitable footwear and floors when material with minimum ignition energies less than 100 mJ are being handled. Unintended build-up of bulk powder at the base of the dryer should be prevented. Such accumulation can be detected using a level detector.

• The spray mechanism contains parts which may cause frictional heating. The rotor mechanism may be a source of oil contamination which can result in a marked decrease in the thermal stability of the product.

• An explosible dust cloud will ignite spontaneously if the temperature is high enough. The minimum ignition temperature (MIT) of a dust cloud is measured in the Godbert-Greenwald furnace test (Section 2.1 — page 14). Ignition of the cloud will be prevented if the inlet air temperature is limited to a value 50°C below the measured MIT[15].

• Material can be deposited on roofs or walls of dryers and exposed to temperatures high enough to cause exothermic decomposition. If this progresses to red heat, burning material that breaks away can act as an ignition source in downstream units. Dryers should be operated so that layers do not form in zones where they are subjected to high temperatures[15]. For layers of powder not exposed for long periods a safety margin of 20°C below the measured layer ignition temperature (Section 2.1 — page 14) is usually satisfactory[15].

• Material should not be allowed to form bulky deposits in the dryer chamber. However, bulking may happen in the cyclone, filter or in packages. Exothermic decomposition may continue in the middle, eventually leading to smouldering and fire, if the initial temperature is above a product- and size-dependent value. The maximum safe discharge temperature of material from the dryer is governed by the temperature measured in tests that assess the capability of bulk powders to undergo thermal decomposition[15,74].

• In order to prevent ignition by 'thermite' sparks, aluminium, magnesium, titanium and light alloys containing these metals should not be used, unless rust can be excluded from the plant.

• All electrical equipment should be compatible with the materials used and the methods for handling them.

• Explosion protection of the dryer is possible by venting. There are circumstances where explosion venting may not be viable (Section 2.2 — page 20). Typical explosion venting precautions are:

(a) The reduced explosion pressure, P_{red}, that the dryer chamber can withstand should be known; typical values are 0.2–0.7 bar g.

(b) Explosion panels should occupy as much of the top area of the dryer chamber as is found necessary by using a vent calculation method. The area beneath the hot air inlet should not be used as a vent so as to prevent damage to the air inlet if an explosion takes place. No other structure should obstruct the top area, through the vent. The vent opening pressure, P_{stat}, should be known, eg 0.1 bar g.

(c) Vent closures should be securely tethered to the main structure if they are capable of acting as missiles, eg panels in the T-section frame.

(d) The forces holding the closure, including its mass, should be as low as is practicable (kg/m^2). Any snow, corrosion or contamination should be prevented from interfering with the action of the vent.

(e) Lifting of vents must shut the air flow and stop the rotary valve at the dryer product outlet.

(f) Water sprays should be fitted in the dryer chamber to control fires and smouldering.

CYCLONE (SECTION 6.8.1 — page 146)

Dust entrained in the hot exhaust from the dryer is separated out in the cyclone. Burning material from the dryer can be transported into the cyclone and ignite an explosible dust cloud there. Explosion venting is an option that can be used unless it is impracticable.

● The reduced explosion pressure that the cyclone and all connecting ductwork can withstand must be known, eg 0.2–0.7 bar g.

● Vents should be fitted to surfaces in the cyclone to which the flame has ready access, eg the shoulder of the cyclone or the top. The area obstructed by the air outlet duct should not be used as part of the vent.

● In this example the cyclone outlet duct can also be protected. Vents equal in area to the cross-sectional area of the duct should be placed as recommended in the appropriate guidance (Section 6.3 — page 121).

● The opening requirements of the vent closure are as for the dryer chamber.

● Lifting of the explosion vent should stop all rotary valves to prevent passage of burning or smouldering material to the product collection point.

● If there is a long pipe between the cyclone and the dryer consideration must be given to isolating the cyclone from the dryer in the event of an explosion (see Section 6.3 on page 121).

DUST COLLECTOR (SECTION 6.8.2 — page 147)

The dust collector removes final traces of product from the exhaust air and passes clean air to the atmosphere. Hot particles and sparks from the dryer can ignite a dust cloud in the collector. In this example, the dust enters near the top of the tapered section at the base of the collector, and it is in this area that high concentrations of dust are most likely to be found. The explosion vent should not be obstructed by internal fitments such as filter bags, so that the explosion has unimpeded access to the vent.

• The reduced explosion pressure that the collector and all connected parts, including door latches, can withstand should be known, eg 0.4–0.7 bar g.

• The vent should be fitted at the top of the shaped section of the collector where the explosible cloud is most likely to be localized and where ignition is most likely to take place. The nearer the vent can be positioned to the ignition point the lower the explosion pressure inside the collector will be. The vent area should be calculated by a suitable method when the vent bursting pressure, P_{stat}, is known, eg 0.1 bar g and the free volume of the collector is known.

• The vent closure can be of any appropriate type.

• The vent should be positioned to direct the explosion to a safe place, with entry to a safe area around the discharge point restricted during normal operation. Nearby plant and thoroughfares may restrict the choice for vent position.

• A deflector plate can be fitted at the vent discharge point (Section 7.6 — page 184). This must be of robust construction capable of withstanding a pressure shock of 0.2 bar; it can be erected vertically or at 45° and should be fitted close to the ground or floor and extend 2 m above the top of the vent opening and 1 m on each side.

EXAMPLE B: MILLING SYSTEM
The milling system is shown schematically in Figure 8.2. The unit is in five parts:
• Charging hood and kibbler;
• Mill;
• Cyclone and dust bag;
• Blender;
• Drum filling point.

CHARGING HOOD AND KIBBLER
There is a significant risk of ignition in the kibbler and the possibility of a dust cloud in the charge hood. As well as taking the precautions necessary to avoid ignition by static electricity (see Example A), safety will need to be based on provision of an explosion-protected charging cubicle. The charging hood should be fitted with doors which are closed after loading and which are interlocked with the kibbler drive to prevent the unit from running until the doors are closed.

• Material should be emptied into the charging hopper inside a closed charging

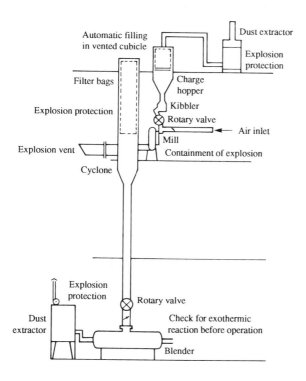

Figure 8.2   Milling plant (schematic).

cubicle using a drum topping device that cannot operate until the cubicle doors are closed.

• The cubicle should be fitted with an appropriate explosion vent. The reduced explosion pressure which can be withstood must be known as must the bursting pressure of the vent closure. The vent closure should be as light as is practicable.

• A rotary valve below the kibbler will prevent an explosion inside the mill propagating into the charging hopper.

• The dust collector in the dust extraction system attached to the charging cubicle will require explosion venting, as will the duct between these units. Keeping the dust concentration below 10 g/m^3 may be a satisfactory basis for safety in the ducting, as long as the duct is kept free of powder deposits that could be raised into a dust cloud.

THE MILL (SECTION 6.8.4 — page 149)

The basis of safety for the mill can be based on containment, as long as explosions are prevented from propagating into adjacent plant. The mill should be capable of withstanding the maximum explosion pressure, P_{max} (eg 7 bar g), if this is used. In this example the safety is based on the explosion venting of this small volume into the cyclone and filter volumes. The vent on the cyclone should be directly opposite the entry pipe from the mill.

CYCLONE AND DUST BAGS

In this example the cyclone and collector are connected and must be treated as one unit. If explosion venting is a valid option for explosion protection, then either a vent large enough to accommodate the entire vessel can be fitted in the cyclone or two vents can be used, one in the cyclone and one close to the filter bags and venting on the dirty side. The reduced explosion pressure that the unit can withstand, eg 0.4–0.7 bar g, and the opening pressure of the vent closure, P_{stat}, eg 0.1 bar g must be known. An appropriate vent sizing technique is used to calculate the vent area based on the free volume of the vessel. Venting of the collectors is discussed in Section 6.8.2 on page 147.

Explosion precautions in a cyclone are discussed in Example A.

BLENDER

Material from the cyclone is fed by a rotary valve through a duct into the top of the blender. Dust clouds can be generated inside a blender; possible ignition sources include thermal instability of the bulk powder and incandescent particles from upstream units. It is difficult to avoid these ignition sources with total effectiveness. One option is to leave the blender standing for 12 hours. In this time any exothermic activity should be detectable by signs of smoke, fume, flame or smouldering.

Explosion venting of blenders is generally not satisfactory because of the large amount of material inside them. In the event of a dust cloud explosion much of this inventory can be entrained in the gas movement and ejected into the open where it can be ignited by the initial vented explosion producing extensive flame. Voluminous dust clouds are theoretically possible in these circumstances. Venting into a confining vented room is particularly not recommended because the dust cloud ejected from the blender would be turbulent, possibly pressurized to above ambient and subject to ignition by a large jet flame.

If ignition sources cannot be excluded in the blender then, since venting is not a practical option, an alternative basis of safety must be identified, eg suppression, containment, inert gas blanketing.

The dust extraction system from the blender will require explosion venting of the duct and the filter — see Example A.

DRUM FILLING POINT

Operatives at drum filling points should be protected against the danger of fire or explosion. Anti-static precautions should be taken (see Example A) and a dust extraction system employed.

EXAMPLE C: SPIN FLASH DRYER

The system is shown schematically in Figure 8.3 on pages 202–203.

THE DRYING CHAMBER

The product is dried by being agitated in the drying chamber while a flow of hot air is passed through the bed of paste. As the paste dries the agitation breaks the product into small pieces and when it is sufficiently dry it is carried in the air stream to a cyclone and then a dust collector.

Some of the ignition sources in the drying chamber are as discussed in Example A:

- Danger of fuel from the natural gas burners collecting in the drying chamber.
- Exothermic decomposition of the product due to too high a drying temperature. Temperatures measured in appropriate tests will limit the practical temperature after subtraction of an adequate safety margin[15].
- Frictional ignition from contact between the rotary agitator and other parts of the equipment or tramp metal.
- Electrostatic discharges from charge accumulation due to movement of the powder.

Total exclusion of ignition sources is not possible and explosion protection is necessary. The vent area in the drying chamber can be calculated by any appropriate method. If an explosion door is fitted this should be as light as is practicable, eg < 10 kg/m^2. If heavier doors are fitted, say 48 kg/m^2, then the vent area will need enlarging (Section 7.1.4 — page 166). The door should be positioned above the level of the agitator. The opening pressure of the vent door should be known, and the reduced explosion pressure that the dryer chamber will withstand, eg 1.8 bar g.

Opening of the door should cause automatic shut-down of the plant. The explosion should be vented to a safe place. (See Example A.)

THE CYCLONE

The main risk is the appearance of burning material from the dryer; venting is the most suitable precaution, as discussed in Example A.

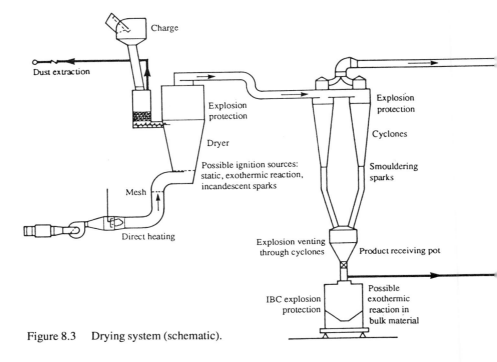

Figure 8.3   Drying system (schematic).

The reduced explosion pressure that the cyclone can withstand should be the same as the drying chamber, as should that of the intervening ductwork, eg 1.8 bar g.

The opening pressure of the vent closure should be known and the vent sized by an appropriate method. The vent closure should be supported internally to guard against vacuum inside the unit by a 15 × 15 mesh. The process should shut down automatically if the vent opens.

DUST FILTER
Venting of the dust filter is as described in Example 1.

PRODUCT-RECEIVING POT
This vessel receives product directly from the cyclones and feeds it to the blender via a rotary valve. It is impossible to guarantee the absence of burning products in this unit, and thus ignition sources cannot be avoided. Safety can be based on venting or containment by means of rotary valves.

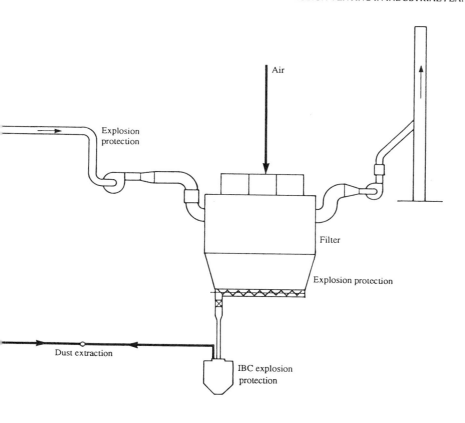

In this case the volume of the pot is small and it is a relatively strong vessel, capable of containing an explosion if the feed lines from the cyclone become partially blocked. The volume of the cyclones and connecting ducts is relatively large, and thus the powder delivery ducts from the cyclones can act as explosion vents. In this case the cyclone can be regarded as a duct fitted to an explosion vent. The vent on the cyclone is fitted on the top. This approach is considered to be satisfactory because every attempt is made to keep the vents, ie delivery ducts, at the pot open all the time. Powder blockage in the cyclone and ducting must be minimized, although the vessel is strong enough to contain an explosion. The strength of the receiving pot should be high.

BLENDER
The explosion precautions for a blender are discussed in Example B.

INTERMEDIATE BULK CONTAINERS (IBCs)
These can be protected by suppressant injected through the filler pipes.

9. REFERENCES

1. Field, P., 1982, *Dust explosions* (Vol. 4 of *Handbook of powder technology*) (Elsevier, ISSN 0167 3785).
2. Abbott, J.A., *BMHB survey of dust fire and explosions in the UK 1979–84* (British Materials Handling Board, ISBN 0 85624 455 4).
3. Porter, B., 1989, Industrial incidents, Paper presented at *Dust Explosions: Assessment, Prevention and Protection*, 24th November, London (IBC Technical Services Ltd).
4. Beck, H. and Jeske, A., 1982, Documentation on dust explosions — analysis and description of individual cases, *BIA — Report 4/82* (Hrsg. Berufsgenossenschaftliches Institut für Arbeitssicherheit — BIA, Sankt Augustin).
5. Jeske, A. and Beck, H., 1987, Documentation on dust explosions — analysis and description of individual cases, *BIA — Report 2/87* (Hrsg. Berufsgenossenschaftliches Institut für Arbeitssicherheit — BIA, Sankt Augustin).
6. Jeske, A. and Beck, H., 1989, Evaluation of dust explosions in the Federal Republic of Germany, *Europex Newsletter No. 9* (European Information Centre for Explosion Protection), 2.
7. Bartknecht, W., 1981, *Explosions: course, prevention, protection* (Springer-Verlag, ISBN 0 387 10216 7).
8. Bartknecht, W., 1989, *Dust explosions: course, prevention, protection* (Springer-Verlag, ISBN 0 387 50100 2).
9. Eckhoff, R.K., 1991, *Dust explosions in the process industries* (Butterworth Heinemann, ISBN 0 7506 1109 X).
10. Cashdollar, K.L. and Hertzberg, M. (Eds), 1987, *Industrial dust explosions*, ASTM Special Technical Publication 958 (American Society of Testing and Materials).
11. Nagy, J. and Verakis, H.C., 1983, *Development and control of dust explosions, Occupational safety and health, No. 8* (Marcel Dekker Inc, ISBN 0 8247 7004 8).
12. Lunn, G.A., 1984, *Venting of gas and dust explosions — a review* (Institution of Chemical Engineers, Rugby, UK, ISBN 0 85295 179 5).
13. Schofield, C. and Abbott, J.A., 1988, *Guide to dust explosion prevention and protection. Part 2 — Ignition, inerting, suppression and isolation* (Institution of Chemical Engineers, Rugby, UK, ISBN 0 85295 222 8).
14. Lunn, G.A., 1988, *Guide to dust explosion prevention and protection. Part 3 — Venting of weak explosions and the effect of vent ducts* (Institution of Chemical Engineers, Rugby, UK, ISBN 0 85295 230 9).
15. Abbott, J.A., 1990, *Prevention of fires and explosions in dryers* (Institution of Chemical Engineers, Rugby, UK, ISBN 0 85295 257 0).

16. NFPA, 1988, *Guide for venting of deflagrations (NFPA 68)* (National Fire Protection Association, Quincy, USA).

17. VDI, 1984, *Pressure release of dust explosions (VDI 3673)* (Verein Deutscher Ingenieure — Kommission Reinhaltung der Luft, Germany).

18. Schofield, C., 1984, *Guide to dust explosion prevention and protection. Part 1 — Venting* (Institution of Chemical Engineers, Rugby, UK, ISBN 0 85295 177 9).

19. Hertzberg, M. and Cashdollar, K.L., 1987, Introduction to dust explosions, in *Industrial dust explosions*, K.L. Cashdollar and M. Hertzberg (Eds), ASTM Special Technical Publication 958 (American Society of Testing and Materials).

20. ISSA, 1987, *Rules for dust explosion protection for machines and equipment — preventive and constructional measures* (International Social Security Agency, Mannheim, Germany).

21. Research Report, 1980, *Combustion and explosion characteristics of dusts* (Schiftenreike des Hauptverbandes der gewerblicken Berufs-genoss-enschaften e.V. Bonn, Germany).

22. Banhegyi, M. and Egyedi, J., 1983, Method for determining the explosive limits of a mixture of coal dust, methane and inert matter, Paper presented at the *20th International Conference of Safety in Mines Research Institutes*, Sheffield, UK, 3–7 October.

23. Feng, K.K., 1983, Hazardous characteristics of Canadian coal dusts, Paper presented at the *20th International Conference of Safety in Mines Research Institutes*, Sheffield, UK, 3–7 October.

24. Foniok, R., 1983, Explosiveness and ignitability of hybrid dispersive mixtures and integral mixtures of coal dust, Paper presented at the *20th International Conference of Safety in Mines Research Institutes*, Sheffield, UK, 3–7 October.

25. BS 5958, (Part 1: 1980 (1987), Part 2: 1983), *Code of practice for control of undesirable static electricity* (British Standards Institution).

26. Glarner, T., 1983, Temperatureinfluss auf das Explosions — und Zünd — verhalten brennbarer Stäube, *Diss. ETH Zurich Nr. 7350.*

27. BS 6467, (Part 1: 1985, Part 2: 1988), *Electrical apparatus with protection by enclosure for use in the presence of combustible dusts* (British Standards Institution).

28. Radandt, S., 1982, Dust explosions in silos, Paper presented at *The Control and Prevention of Dust Explosions*, Basel, 16–17 November (IBC Technical Services Ltd).

29. Heinrich, H.J., 1966, Bemassuag von Druckentlastungsofftugsen zum Schutz explosions-gefahrdeter Anlagen in der Chemischem Industrie, *Chemie-In-Techn*, 38: 1125.

30. Donat, C., 1971, *Staub-Reinbalt Luft*, 31: 154.

31. Simpson, L.L., 1986, Equations for the VDI and Bartknecht nomograms, *Plant/Operations Progress*, 5: 49.

32. Gibson, N. and Harris, G.F.P., 1976, The calculation of dust explosion vents, *Chem Eng Prog*, November, 62.

33. Cubbage, P.A. and Simmonds, W.A., 1955, An investigation of explosion reliefs for industrial drying ovens. 1., *Gas Council Research Communications GC23*.

34. Lunn, G.A. *et al*, 1988, Using the K_{st} nomographs to estimate the venting requirements in weak dust handling equipment, *J Loss Prev Proc Ind*, 1 (3): 123.

35. Swift, I. and Epstein, M., 1987, Performance of low pressure explosion vents, *Plant/Operations Progress*, 6: 98.

36. Swift, I., 1988, Design explosion vents easily and accurately, *Chemical Engineering*, April 11 issue, 63.

37. Lunn, G.A., 1989, Methods for sizing dust explosion vent areas: a comparison when reduced explosion pressures are low, *J Loss Prev Proc Ind*, 2: 200.

38. Radandt, S., 1986, Paper presented at *Dust Explosion Venting*, Amsterdam, 17–19 November (Europex seminar/course).

39. Radandt, S., 1985, Explosion relief elongated silos, Paper presented at *A Practical Introduction to Gas and Dust Explosion Venting*, Frankfurt, 3–4 June (Europex).

40. Bartknecht, W., 1986, Pressure venting of dust explosions in large vessels, *Plant/Operations Progress*, 5 (4): 196.

41. Scholl, E., 1992, The technique of explosion venting, much more than just a set of nomographs, Paper presented at the *First World Seminar on Explosion Phenomenon and Practical Application of Protection Techniques*, Brussels (Europex).

42. Pineau, J.P. *et al*, 1986, Influence on gas and dust explosion development of lengthening and presence of obstacles in closed or vented vessels, Paper presented at the *5th International Symposium on Loss Prevention and Safety Promotion in the Process Industries*, Cannes, 15–19 September.

43. AFNOR, 1986, Farming-buildings and storage equipment — silo safety — attenuation of explosion effects by discharge vents — calculation of the vent areas, *U54–540* (Association Française de Normalisation).

44. Eckhoff, R.K., 1986, Sizing dust explosion vents. The need for a new approach based on risk assessment, *Bulk Solids Handling*, 6: 913.

45. Eckhoff, R.K., 1988, A differentiated approach to sizing of dust explosion vents: Influence of ignition source location with particular reference to large, slender silos, *Industrial dust explosions*, K.L. Cashdollar and M. Hertzberg (Eds), ASTM Special Technical Publication 958 (American Society of Testing and Materials).

46. Bartknecht, W., *Massnahmen gegen gefahrliche Auswirkungen von Staubexplosionen in Silos und Behaltern*, Jahresbericht 1985 zum BMF/HdA-Forschungsvorhaben vom Februar 1986.

47. Siwek, R., 1989, Dust explosion venting for dusts pneumatically conveyed into vessels, *Plant/Operations Progress*, 8 (3): 129.

48. Eckhoff, R.K. and Fuhre, K., 1984, Dust explosion experiments in a vented 500 m^3 silo cell, *J Occupational Accidents*, 6: 229.

49. Gardner, B.R. *et al*, 1986, Explosion development and deflagration to detonation transition in coal dust/air suspensions, Paper presented at the *21st Symposium (International) on Combustion* (Combustion Institute), 335.

50. Cybulski, W., 1975, *Coal dust explosions and their suppression* (Bureau of Mines,

USA for the National Centre for Scientific, Technical and Economic Information, Warsaw, Poland).

51. Swift, I., 1989, NFPA 68 Guide for venting of deflagrations: what's new and how it affects you, *J Loss Prev Proc Ind*, 2: 5.

52. NFPA, 1978, Guide for explosion venting, *NFPA 68–1978* (National Fire Protection Association, USA).

53. Eckhoff, R.K., Fuhre, K. and Pedersen, G.H., 1987, Dust explosion experiments in a vented 236 m^3 silo cell, *J Occupational Accidents*, 9: 161.

54. Tonkin, P.S. and Berlemont, F.J., 1972, Dust explosions in a large scale cyclone plant, *Fire Research Note 942* (Fire Research Station, Borehamwood, UK).

55. Eckhoff, R.K., 1990, Sizing of dust explosion vents in the process industries. Advances made during the 1980s, *J Loss Prev Proc Ind*, 3: 268.

56. Lunn, G.A. and Cairns, F., 1985, The venting of dust explosions in a dust collector, *J Hazardous Materials*, 12: 87.

57. Schmalz, F., 1982, Grinding and mixing plants, spray driers, Paper presented at *The Control and Prevention of Dust Explosions*, Basle, 16–17 November (IBC Technical Services Ltd).

58. Britton, L.G. and Kirby, D.C., 1989, Analysis of a dust deflagration, *Plant/Operations Progress*, 8 (3): 177.

59. Vogl, A., 1989, How effective are explosion relief stacks?, Paper presented at *Dust Explosion Protection*, Antwerp, 11–13 September (Europex International Symposium).

60. HSE, 1976, Dust explosions in factories, *Health and Safety at Work Booklet No. 22* (HMSO).

61. ICI, 1982, Dust explosion venting — sizing and design of vents and closures, *Process Safety Guide No. 9*.

62. Degood, R. and Chatrathi, K., 1990, A comparative analysis of test work studying factors influencing pressures developed in vented deflagrations, Paper presented at *AIChE Summer National Meeting*, San Diego, August 18–22.

63. Brown, K.C. and Wilde, D.G., 1955, Dust explosions in factories: the protection of plant by hinged explosion doors, *Research Report No. 119* (Safety in Mines Research Establishment).

64. Buckland, I.G. and Tonkin, P.S., 1982, The use of wall mounted inertia vents to mitigate explosion pressures, *Note No. 72/82* (Building Research Establishment).

65. Brown, K.C. and Curzon, G.E., 1963, Dust explosions in factories: explosion vents in pulverised fuel plants, *SMRE Research Report No. 212*.

66. Lunn, G.A., Crowhurst, D. and Hey, M., 1988, The effect of vent ducts on the reduced explosion pressures of vented dust explosions, *J Loss Prev Proc Ind*, 1 (4): 182.

67. Hey, M., 1991, The pressure relief of dust explosions through large diameter ducts and the effect of changing the position of the ignition source, *J Loss Prev Proc Ind*, 4 (4): 217.

68. Alfert, F., 1989, Venting without external fire by means of a Q-pipe, Paper presented

at *Dust Explosion Protection*, Antwerp, 11–13 September (Europex International Symposium).

69. HSE, 1983, *Corn starch dust explosion at General Foods Limited, Banbury, Oxfordshire, 18 November 1981*, Report by HM Factory Inspectorate (HMSO).

70. NFPA, 1976, *Fire protection handbook*, Fourteenth edition, Gordon P. McKinnon (Ed) (National Fire Protection Association, Boston, Mass., USA).

71. Harmanny, A., 1989, Flame jet hazards, Paper presented at *Dust Explosion Protection*, Antwerp, 11–13 September (Europex International Symposium).

72. Hattwig, H., 1980, Investigations on the recoil of vented vessels, Paper presented at *Loss Prevention and Safety Promotion in the Process Industries, 3rd International Symposium*, Basle, September (Swiss Soc of Chem Inds).

73. Eckhoff, R.K. *et al*, 1983, Maize starch explosion experiments in a vented 500 m^3 storage bin, *Report CMI 823307–1* (Chrs Michelson Institute, Fantoft, Norway).

74. Maddison, N., 1991, Safety consciousness in powder drying, *Processing*, June 1991, 15.

NOTE

The Library and Information Service of the Institution of Chemical Engineers in Rugby, UK, offers a worldwide service for the supply of these references.

APPENDIX — DEFINITIONS

EXPLOSIBILITY

The ability of a dust to take part in a cloud explosion when dispersed in air at a suitable concentration and in the presence of an effective ignition source. It denotes both a qualitative assessment of this ability — either explosible or non-explosible; and a quantitative measure of the likely explosion violence — usually the rate of pressure rise in an enclosed explosion. Standard tests are described in Chapter 3.

MAXIMUM EXPLOSION PRESSURE, P_{max}

The maximum pressure measured during an enclosed explosion at the optimum dust concentration in air. Standard tests are described in Chapter 3.

MAXIMUM RATE OF PRESSURE RISE, $(dP/dt)_{max} V^{1/3}$

The maximum rate of pressure rise measured during an enclosed explosion at the optimum dust concentration in air. Standard tests are described in Chapter 3.

THE K_{st} VALUE

A dust-specific measure of the explosibility, in units of bar m s^{-1}, and calculated using the equation:

$$K_{st} = (dP/dt)_{max} \ V^{1/3}$$

where V is the vessel volume. The equation is the so-called 'cubic' or 'cube-root' law. The K_{st} value is considered to be volume independent. The measurement is described in Chapter 3.

THE ST GROUPS

A grouping of explosible dusts according to the St value. See Chapters 3 and 4.

VENT BURSTING PRESSURE, P_{stat}

The pressure at which the vent closure bursts under static conditions. See Chapter 4.

REDUCED EXPLOSION PRESSURE, P_{red}

The pressure to which venting requirements are designed to limit the explosion pressure inside a vented enclosure. See Chapter 4.

VENT RATIO

A basic method of estimating vent areas using the ratio: vent area/vessel volume. See Chapter 4.

***K* FACTOR**

A basic method of estimating vent areas using the ratio: area of cross-section of vessel/area of vent. See Chapter 4.

NOMOGRAPH

A chart, or diagram, of scaled lines or curves used to help in calculations, comprising three scales in which a line joining values on two determines a third.

INDEX